Shakespe

ROMEO AND JULIET

*A shortened and simplified version
in modern English*

by

John & Leela Hort

THE KABET PRESS

1986

First published 1986 by The Kabet Press

By the same authors:

TWELFTH NIGHT
HENRY V

British Library Cataloguing in Publication Data

Hort, John
    Shakespeare's Romeo and Juliet : a shortened and
    simplified version in modern English. — (The
    Inessential Shakespeare)
    I. Title   II. Hort, Leela   III. Shakespeare,
    William. Romeo and Juliet   IV. Series
    822'.914   PR6058.0718/

    ISBN 0-948662-02-6

Permission must be obtained and a fee paid before this play is performed
in public, whether or not there is an admission fee.
Details can be obtained from:

                The Kabet Press
                239 Bramcote Lane
                Wollaton
                Nottingham NG8 2QL

PROFESSIONAL PRODUCERS
                Please write to The Kabet Press

    NB   It is illegal to perform this play or to read it publicly
           unless written permission has been obtained.

           It is illegal to copy the play in whole or in part by
           any reproduction process.

Printed by The Russell Press Ltd., Bertrand Russell House,
Gamble Street, Nottingham NG7 4ET

To Gilly and Margaret, in
gratitude for all your help and
encouragement

CONTENTS

PEOPLE IN THE PLAY

The Montagues and the Capulets are two important families
in Verona who have been enemies for a long time.

Chorus	The Chorus introduces the play.
Prince Escalus	The ruler of Verona.
Mercutio	A young relation of the prince, a friend of Romeo.
Paris	Another young man, also a relation of the prince, who wants to marry Juliet.

THE MONTAGUES

Montague	Head of the Montague family.
Lady Montague	His wife.
Romeo	Their son.
Benvolio	Their nephew, a friend of Romeo and Mercutio.
Abram	A servant in the Montague household.
Balthasar	Romeo's servant.

THE CAPULETS

Capulet	Head of the Capulet family.
Lady Capulet	His wife.
Juliet	Their daughter, aged 13.
Tybalt	Their nephew.
Nurse	A woman who has looked after Juliet ever since she was born.
Peter	Servant to the nurse.
Sampson **Gregory** **Anthony** **Potpan** }	Servants in the Capulet household.

Friar Laurence	A Franciscan friar.
Friar John	Another friar.
Apothecary	He makes and sells medicines. (We have used the word "Apothecary" because there is no modern equivalent.)
Simon Catling **Hugh Rebeck** **James Soundpost** }	Musicians.

Citizens of Verona, Masked Men, Guests, Musicians, Servants, Officers, Friends of Capulet, of Montague, of Mercutio and Benvolio, and of Tybalt.

NOTE
The names of characters who appear in each scene are given in a box at the beginning of the scene. Non-speaking parts are in brackets.

In ACT ONE "c" or "m" indicates that a person (or group) is a member of, or is closely connected with, the Capulet or Montague household.

Chorus Our play is set in the beautiful city of Verona, where an old quarrel between two great families has broken out once again in violence and bloodshed. From the families of these two deadly enemies come a pair of young lovers, whose ill-fated lives end in tragedy. Only with their deaths is their parents' hatred buried.

ACT ONE

SCENE 1
A Street in Verona

Sampson c	Capulet c
Gregory c	Lady Capulet c
Abram m	Montague m
(Servant m)	Lady Montague m
Benvolio m	Prince Escalus
Tybalt c	(Attendants)
Citizens c & m	Romeo m

[*Sampson* and *Gregory* come in. They are servants in the CAPULET household, and they are wearing swords]

Sampson Damn it, Gregory, we're not going to be treated like dogs.

Gregory Certainly not. I shan't wear a collar.

Sampson Do you mean you won't be a priest?

Gregory I'd rather have a rope round my neck than a dog-collar, any day.

Sampson Those Montague dogs upset me.

Gregory What? They make you fall over, do they?

Sampson Of course not. I'll stand up to any Montague that comes along.

Gregory What about the women?

Sampson Well, I'd rather lie down with the women.

Gregory Look! Here come a couple of Montagues. Draw your sword.

Sampson [*He draws his sword*] Right! You pick a quarrel with them, and I'll back you up.

Gregory You mean, you'll back down.

Sampson Don't let's break the law. Let *them* start something.

Gregory I'll scowl at them, and see how they take it.

Sampson And I'll do this. [*He makes a rude gesture*] If they take that lying down, they're cowards.

1

[Abram and another Servant come in. They are members of the MONTAGUE household]

Abram *[To Sampson]* Are you doing that at *us*, sir?

Sampson *[He hums and makes the gesture again]* Hmmmm...

Abram I said, are you doing that at *us*, sir?

Sampson *[He whispers to Gregory]* Would I be breaking the law if I said "Yes"?

Gregory *[Whispers]* Yes!

Sampson *[To Abram]* No, sir. I'm not doing it at *you*, sir. I'm just doing it. Sir!

Gregory *[To Abram]* Do you want a fight, sir?

Abram A fight? No, sir.

Sampson Well, if you do, I'll give you one. My master's as good as yours.

Abram He's certainly not better.

Gregory *[He sees Tybalt coming. To Sampson]* Here comes one of our master's relations. Say "Ours is better".

Sampson Ours is better.

Abram That's a lie!

Sampson *[To Abram and the Servant]* Draw your swords, if you call yourselves men. Gregory, remember what I taught you. *[The four men draw their swords and start fighting]*

[Benvolio comes in and draws his sword]

Benvolio Stop it, you fools! Do you realise what you're doing?

[Tybalt comes in]

Tybalt *[To Benvolio]* What, fighting with the servants? You'd do better to turn round, Benvolio, and fight me. *[He draws his sword]*

Benvolio I'm only trying to keep the peace. Put your sword away, or else use it to help me separate this lot.

Tybalt I like that! Talking of peace with a sword in your hand. I hate the word, as much as I hate hell, all Montagues and you — you coward! *[He fights with Benvolio]*

[Some Citizens come in with sticks and other weapons, and join in the fighting. They shout "Down with the Capulets!", "Down with the Montagues!" etc. etc. Then Capulet comes in wearing a dressing-gown, with Lady Capulet]

Capulet What's all this? Bring me my sword!

Lady Capulet What you need is a crutch, not a sword.

[Montague and Lady Montague come in. Montague has a sword]

Capulet Give me my sword, I say! I won't have old Montague mocking me.

Montague I'll get you, Capulet. *[To his wife, who is holding him back]* Let me go!

Lady Montague No! You shan't move an inch.

[*Prince Escalus comes in with his Attendants*]

Prince Escalus [*He speaks while they are still fighting*] Citizens of Verona, how dare you disturb the peace with your fighting... [*He shouts*] Will you listen to me! Listen, I say! [*They become quiet*] You miserable wretches, cooling your tempers with your neighbours' blood! Put down your weapons, and listen to me. You, old Capulet, and you, Montague, this is the third time that your ridiculous quarrel has disturbed our quiet streets and forced Verona's respectable old citizens to get out their weapons. If you disturb the peace once more, I promise you you will pay for it with your lives. Now go, all of you. Capulet, come with me. And Montague, I want to see you this afternoon, in Freetown. [*To all the others*] Now, go! You remain here at your peril.

[*They all go out, except Montague, Lady Montague and Benvolio*]

Montague Who began this? Were you here when it started, nephew?

Benvolio Your servants were already fighting with the Capulets when I got here, so I tried to stop them. Then that firebrand Tybalt came rushing in, waving his sword about and threatening me. Then more and more people joined in, until the Prince came and broke it up.

Lady Montague Where is Romeo? Have you seen him today? I'm so glad he wasn't here.

Benvolio I couldn't sleep last night, madam, so I got up early and went for a walk. While I was out, I saw your son in the sycamore woods, to the west of the city. I went towards him, but as soon as he saw me, he disappeared among the trees. Clearly, neither of us wanted company, so I left him.

Montague He's been seen there quite often lately, poor unhappy boy. But as soon as it is light, he comes home, shuts himself in his room and draws the curtains — turning day into night. If he doesn't get some help and advice, I fear he may become ill.

Benvolio Do you know why he's like this, uncle?

Montague No, and I can't find out either. He keeps his thoughts to himself, and won't take anyone into his confidence.

Benvolio Look! Here he comes. If you go, I'll do my best to find out what's wrong. [*Montague and Lady Montague hurry out. Romeo comes in the other side*] Good morning, cousin.

Romeo Is it still morning?

Benvolio It's just nine o'clock.

Romeo How slowly time passes when you're unhappy. Was that my father?

Benvolio Yes, it was. Romeo, what is it that's making you so sad?

Romeo Not having the thing that would make me happy.

Benvolio Are you in love?

Romeo No, out.

Benvolio Of love?

Romeo No. Out of luck in love.

Benvolio Isn't it a pity that love, which seems so gentle, should in fact be so cruel.

Romeo Yes, and blind Cupid always gets his own way... Where shall we have dinner? [*He looks around*] Good God! What's been happening here? No — don't tell me: I've heard it all before. But it's nothing, compared to the state I'm in. [*He sighs*] I suppose you could call mine a sort of hateful love, or a waking sleep or a freezing fire. In fact, I'm much too much in love to enjoy this quarrel... Why don't you laugh at me, Benvolio?

Benvolio I feel more like crying, cousin.

Romeo Why?

Benvolio Because you're so unhappy.

Romeo You can blame love for that. And your sympathy only makes it worse. My dear Ben, I tell you, love is a fire, sparkling in lovers' eyes; it is a sea, fed by lovers' tears; it is a gentle madness, both bitter and sweet. Goodbye, cousin! [*He starts to go*]

Benvolio You can't leave me like this. I'll come with you, Romeo.

Romeo I'm not Romeo. I've lost myself. Romeo is somewhere else.

Benvolio Come on, be serious. Who are you in love with?

Romeo What? Shall I pull a long face and tell you?

Benvolio Pull a long face? Of course not. But tell me, seriously, who is it?

Romeo Do you need to remind a sick man to be serious when he's making his will? Well, seriously, I am in love with... a woman.

Benvolio I thought as much.

Romeo A brilliant thought! And let me tell you this: she's pretty.

Benvolio A pretty miss, eh? Well caught!

Romeo But she refuses to be caught — by loving words, or loving looks, or money. Oh, she is beautiful! But when she dies, her beauty will die with her.

Benvolio Has she said she will never get married, then?

Romeo Yes. What a waste! Her beauty will die with her, and since she'll never love anyone, my life is pointless.

Benvolio Take my advice: stop thinking about her.

Romeo You might as well tell me to stop thinking.

Benvolio Look at some other pretty girls.

Romeo But that will only make me think of her even more. Asking me to forget Rosaline is like asking a blind man to forget how precious sight is. No, you'll never get me to forget her.

Benvolio But I shan't give up trying.

4

SCENE 2
Another street in Verona

Capulet c
Paris
Servant c
Benvolio m
Romeo m

[*Capulet, Paris* and a *Servant* come in]

Capulet The Prince has made us swear to keep the peace, which shouldn't be difficult for old men like Montague and me.

Paris And you're so well thought of in Verona. It's a pity you have been enemies for so long... But now, my lord, what do you say to my proposal?

Capulet What I said before. My daughter is not yet fourteen, and she hasn't much experience of the world. Let's wait another two years before we think of marriage.

Paris But girls younger than her are already mothers.

Capulet Yes, but these early marriages often end badly. She is my last surviving child, Paris, and my heir. Win her heart, my boy. My consent is only part of it. If she agrees to marry, I will happily accept her choice... By the way, we shall be having our usual celebration tonight, and I have invited some dear friends to a party. You are most welcome to join us. I promise you, you will meet some lovely young ladies. You should find the experience as refreshing as the arrival of spring! Study them, and choose the best — my daughter will be among them. [*To the Servant*] Here, go round the town and find these people, [*he gives him a paper*] and invite them to our house tonight. [*Capulet and Paris go out*]

Servant Find the people whose names are written here? You might as well expect a fisherman to catch a fish with a pencil, or a painter to paint with a net! I must find an educated person to help me.

[*Benvolio and Romeo come in*]

Benvolio A new pain makes the old one more bearable. What you need is to fall in love again — that'll cure you.

Romeo Cabbage leaves are good for that.

Benvolio For what?

Romeo For a broken leg.

Benvolio Have you gone mad?

Romeo No, but I feel as if I've been put in a strait jacket, shut up in prison, starved, beaten, tortured and... [*He sees the Servant*] Good afternoon, fellow.

Servant Good afternoon, sir. Excuse me, sir, but can you read?

Romeo [*Looking at his palm*] I can read my unhappy fortune!

Servant I suppose you've learnt that by heart, sir! But can you read *writing*?

5

Romeo Yes, if I know the language.

Servant Well, at least you're honest, sir. Goodbye. [*He starts to go*]

Romeo Wait, fellow. Of course I can read. [*He takes the paper and reads*] "Mr and Mrs Martino and their daughters. Count Anselm and his beautiful sisters. The widow, Lady Utruvio. Mr Laventio and his lovely nieces. Mercutio and his brother Valentine. My uncle Capulet, his wife and daughters. My pretty niece Rosaline, and Livia. Mr Valentino and his cousin Tybalt. Lucio and the lively Helena." That's a fine list. Where are they invited?

Servant Up to our house.

Romeo Whose house is "our" house?

Servant My master's, of course.

Romeo [*He laughs*] Of course.

Servant Let me tell you. My master is the great, rich Capulet, and if you're not a Montague, please come and drink a glass of wine with us tonight. Goodbye, sir. [*He goes out*]

Benvolio Aha! So your Rosaline is going to be there, with all the beautiful women of Verona. Go to the party, Romeo, and compare her with the others. You'll soon see that your rose is only a common weed.

Romeo My tears will turn to flames and burn my eyes out before that happens! Someone more beautiful than my Rosaline? Never, since the world began, has the sun shone on so lovely a lady!

Benvolio Nonsense! Wait till you see some of the women at the party tonight.

Romeo All right, I'll go, but only to enjoy the dazzling beauty of my Rosaline.

SCENE 3

A room in Capulet's house

Lady Capulet c
Nurse c
Juliet c
Servant c

[*Lady Capulet and the Nurse come in*]

Lady Capulet Nurse, where's my daughter? Tell her to come here.

Nurse I've already called her, madam. [*She calls out*] My lamb! My pet! Where *is* she? Juliet!

[*Juliet comes in*]

Juliet What is it, mother?

Lady Capulet I want to talk to you alone, Juliet. [*To the Nurse*] Leave us, please, nurse. [*The Nurse starts to go*] No, come back. I think you'd better hear this too. Now, Juliet's not a child any more...

6

Nurse Yes, and I can tell you her age to the hour.

Lady Capulet She's nearly fourteen, isn't she?

Nurse I'll bet fourteen of my teeth she is, except that I haven't got that many left! How long is it till August?

Lady Capulet A fortnight, nurse, plus the odd day or two.

Nurse Odd or even, on the last day of July she'll be fourteen. My Susan and she were exactly the same age. Well, Susan is with God, she was too good for me... But, as I was saying, she'll be fourteen on the day before the harvest festival. It was the day of the earthquake, eleven years ago, the day she was weaned. What a day! I'll never forget it. I was sitting in the sun under the dovecot wall. I'd put some mustard on my nipple. The master and you, madam, were in Mantua. Oh yes, I've still got a good memory. But as I was saying, when she tasted the mustard, she got so cross, and looked so funny, the pretty little fool...! Then the dovecot wall began to shake, and I didn't need any more warning that it was time to move on. That was eleven years ago! She could stand up all by herself, then, and toddle about. Only the day before she'd fallen down and cut her forehead, and my husband — he was always joking, God bless him — picked her up and said, "You've fallen on your face, have you? But you'll be falling in love soon, won't you, Julie?" And do you know? The pretty little thing stopped crying, and said, "Yes". And to think that it's all coming true now! I'll never forget it, not if I live to be a thousand. "Won't you, Julie?" he said, and the little thing stopped crying, and said, "Yes".

Lady Capulet That's enough, nurse.

Nurse Yes, madam... But I can't help laughing, when I think of her stopping crying, and saying, "Yes". And yet she had a lump on her head as big as a marble. Ah, it was a dreadful bang, and she cried bitterly. "Aha!" said my husband. "You've fallen on your face have you? When you're a young lady, you'll be falling in love. Eh, Julie?" And it stopped crying straight away, and said, "Yes".

Juliet I wish *you* would stop, nurse.

Nurse Don't worry, I've finished... But you *were* the prettiest baby I ever nursed. And if I live to see you married one day, I'll be happy.

Lady Capulet Marriage? Why, that's exactly what I want to talk to you about. Tell me, Juliet, what do you feel about getting married?

Juliet I've never thought of such a — such an honour.

Nurse An *honour*! If I wasn't your nurse, I'd say you'd sucked in wisdom with your mother's milk.

Lady Capulet Well, think about it now. There are many girls of your age from good families here in Verona, who are already mothers. I was not much older myself when you were born... But to get to the point: that fine young man Paris wants you to be his wife.

7

Nurse There's a man for you, young lady! Everyone knows how — what a perfect gentleman he is.

Lady Capulet What do you say, Juliet? Can you love him? You'll see him tonight at our party. Study him carefully. You'll find he's a handsome young man, and his eyes will tell you the rest. And a handsome man needs the love of a beautiful wife to make his life complete. Put on a wedding ring, and bind him to you. Then you will share what he has, and lose nothing.

Nurse Lose something? No, women get bigger when they marry!

Lady Capulet Well, Juliet, do you think you can love Paris?

Juliet I'll try to, if I like him. But I'll be guided by you.

[*A Servant comes running in*]

Servant Madam, the guests are here, supper is on the table, you are wanted, people are asking for Miss Juliet, they're cursing Nurse in the kitchen, and everything is in a muddle. I must get back. Please come straight away!

Lady Capulet Yes, yes, we're coming. [*The Servant runs out*] Juliet, Count Paris is waiting for you.

Nurse Go on, girl, go to Paris and be happy.

<table>
<tr><td>SCENE 4
The street in front of Capulet's house</td><td>Benvolio m
Mercutio
Romeo m
(Masked men m)
(Servants m)</td></tr>
</table>

[*Romeo, Mercutio and Benvolio come in with five or six Masked Men, and some Servants with lights and masks*]

Benvolio* Shall we go straight in? Or shall we read our speech out first?

Mercutio* That sort of thing is out of date now. It's about as fashionable as dressing up as Cupid and waving a painted bow about to frighten the ladies. Let them think what they like about us. We'll just have a dance and go.

Romeo I'll carry a light, my heart is too heavy for dancing.

Mercutio But you're a lover. Borrow Cupid's wings, and fly over the floor.

Romeo But Cupid has shot me down. I'm sinking into love.

Mercutio Sinking into your love? That's a rough way to treat a tender thing.

Romeo Love isn't tender. It's rough and piercing.

Mercutio Treat it roughly, then. That's the way to soften it... [*To a Servant*] Now, give me one of those masks to hide my ugly face. [*He puts on a mask*] What do I care what people think of me!

8

Benvolio Let's knock and go in. As soon as we're in, we'll start dancing.

Romeo I'll carry a light. Those with light hearts can do the dancing. Anyway, the spectator has the best view of the game.

Mercutio* Don't be such a stick-in-the-mud. We'll drag you out of — love. Come on, we're burning time.

Romeo What do you mean?

Mercutio We're wasting our torches. Use your common sense.

Romeo My common sense tells me we shouldn't go on with this.

Mercutio And why, may I ask?

Romeo I had a dream last night.

Mercutio So did I.

Romeo What was yours?

Mercutio That dreamers often lie.

Romeo Yes, in bed, asleep, while they dream of things that are true!

Mercutio Ah! I can see Queen Mab has been with you. She's the fairy who turns men's daydreams into dreams. She's a tiny little thing, no bigger than a diamond in a ring, and she drives her carriage over men's noses as they lie asleep. Her carriage is small and delicately made, and she drives it night after night through lovers' brains, to make them dream of love; over lawyers' fingers, to make them dream of money; over ladies' lips, to make them dream of kisses. Sometimes she drives over a soldier's neck, and then he dreams of battles and swords and cutting foreign throats and drinking mugs of beer; then she drums in his ear, and he wakes up in a fright, says a prayer or two, and goes back to sleep again. This is the same Queen Mab who gives young women their first lessons in love, as they lie asleep on their backs. And she —

Romeo Oh, do stop talking such nonsense, Mercutio.

Mercutio Well, dreams *are* nonsense — as empty as air, as changeable as the wind, which chases off to the icy north, gets a cold welcome there, turns back, and heads for the warm south.

Benvolio All this wind of yours is stopping us from going to the party! Supper's over, it'll soon be too late.

Romeo [*To himself*] Better not to go at all. I have a terrible sense of foreboding. I fear that what this evening's adventure begins will end in disaster and death — my death. But I am in God's hands. [*To the others, cheerfully*] Well, let's go in!

Benvolio Go on! Beat the drum.

[*One of the **Masked Men** beats a drum, and they all put masks on and march into Capulet's house*]

---

*It is generally agreed that Benvolio and Mercutio should say these lines.

—MASK.

SCENE 5
A large room in Capulet's house

All from Scene 4 plus:	
2 Servants c	Juliet c
(Other servants c)	Tybalt c
Anthony c	Nurse c
Potpan c	Guest c
Capulet c	(Other Guests)
Lady Capulet c	(Musicians)

SR

[*Servants are clearing away tables, chairs, dishes etc. The Masked Men and the others march in*]

1st Servant Why isn't Potpan here? He's meant to be clearing up. He's a fine helper!

2nd Servant So much for extra hands! And dirty hands at that!

1st Servant [*To the other Servants*] Take away those chairs! Move the sideboard! Deal with the silver! [*To the 2nd Servant*] Be a good fellow, and save me a piece of that marzipan. And get the porter to let Sue and Nell in. [*The 2nd Servant goes out*] Anthony! Potpan!

[*Anthony and Potpan come in*]

Anthony Here I am, my boy!

1st Servant You've been asked for, and called for, and shouted for in the dining room.

Potpan We can't be everywhere. Cheer up, lads! Let's have some fun while we can. [*Anthony and Potpan go out*]

[*Capulet, Lady Capulet, Juliet, Tybalt, Nurse, Guests and Musicians come in*] *SHAKE HANDS — CAP.*

Capulet [*To Benvolio, Mercutio, Romeo and the other Masked Men*] Welcome, gentlemen! [*To the ladies*] Now, ladies! You'd better not say you won't dance. If you do, I'll tell everyone you've got corns...! [*To the Masked Men*] Yes, gentlemen, you are welcome. I used to wear a mask and whisper sweet nothings in a lady's ear once upon a time. But those days are gone. Ah, they're gone! [*To the Musicians*] Music, please! [*To the Servants*] Clear the floor! Light some more candles! Move those tables away! [*Music and dancing*] Open a window, it's much too hot in here. This *is* a pleasant surprise! [*To a Guest*] Come and sit with me, cousin. Our dancing days are over. How long is it since you and I wore masks?

Guest It must be thirty years.

Capulet Surely not. It was at Lucentio's wedding, and that was twenty five years ago.

Guest It was more than that, sir. His eldest son is thirty.

Capulet Really? It seems like only a couple of years since he came of age.

Romeo [*To a Servant, pointing at Juliet and Paris*] Who is that lady over there, dancing with that gentleman?

talking

10

Servant I don't know, sir.

Romeo [*To himself*] Oh, how beautiful she is! She could teach the sun how to shine! She is like some glittering star in the night sky, too precious for this world, outshining all the others. When this dance is over, I'll go to her, and touch her hand, and mine will be blessed. I swear I have never really loved till now.

Tybalt [*Looking at Romeo*] I recognise that voice. He's a Montague. [*To a Servant*] Fetch me my sword. [*The Servant goes out*] How dare he come here, with that face on, to laugh at us? I'll kill him, or I'm no Capulet.

Capulet What's the matter, nephew?

Tybalt [*Pointing at Romeo*] Uncle, he's a Montague, and our enemy. He's come here to make fun of us.

Capulet It's young Romeo, isn't it?

Tybalt Yes, that ruffian Romeo.

Capulet Calm down, nephew. Leave him alone. He's behaving well enough, and I've heard that he's a good lad. I won't have him insulted here in my house, not for all the money in Verona. Take no notice of him, I tell you, and stop looking so angry. It's not right, at a party.

Tybalt Yes, it is, when a villain like that is a guest. I won't put up with him.

Capulet Who's master in this house, eh? You or me? You won't put up with him, indeed! You'll upset the whole party.

Tybalt It's wrong, uncle.

Capulet You cheeky fellow! You know, this kind of thing could get you into trouble. Trust you to argue! [*He claps his hands to encourage the dancers*] That's the way! [*To the Servants*] Let's have some more candles! [*To Tybalt*] I'll calm you down, my lad. [*To the dancers*] That's the way!

Tybalt [*To himself*] It's almost more than I can bear, to have to be patient with this bad-tempered old man. I'll leave. But nothing good shall come of this. [*He goes out*]

Romeo [*To Juliet, taking her hand*] If it is wrong of me to touch you with this rough hand of mine, let me make up for my sin with a kiss.

Juliet You wrong your hand. Its touch is quite enough. You don't need to kiss.

Romeo But I have lips.

Juliet Yes, to speak with.

Romeo But lips can do more than that. Please grant them their wish, or my love will turn to despair.

Juliet I'm not stopping you.

Romeo Then be still, while my prayer is answered. [*He kisses her*] Now I am clear of sin.

Juliet But my lips have taken on your sin.

11

Romeo Sin from my lips? [*He laughs*] Then let me have it back again. [*He kisses her again*]

Nurse [*To **Juliet***] Madam! Madam, your mother wants a word with you.

[***Juliet** goes to **Lady Capulet***]

Romeo [*To the **Nurse***] Who is her mother?

Nurse The lady of the house, young man, and a fine lady too! I nursed her daughter — the girl you've just been talking to. I tell you, whoever gets her will make a good match.

Romeo [*To himself*] What? A Capulet? Oh, God! My life is in my enemy's hands.

Benvolio Come on, Romeo. Let's leave, while things are going well.

Romeo Yes, they can only get worse.

Capulet [*To the **Masked Men***] No, gentlemen, don't talk about going. We are just about to have some refreshments. [*The **Masked Men** insist*] Is that so? Ah well, thank you for coming, gentlemen. Good night. [*To the others*] Come along, now. It's getting late. I'm off to bed. [*They all go out, as **Juliet** and the **Nurse** talk*]

Juliet Come here, nurse. Who is that gentleman? [*She points*]

Nurse Old Tiberio's son.

Juliet And who's that, just going out of the door?

Nurse I think that's young Petruchio.

Juliet [*She points to **Romeo***] And that one, the one who wouldn't dance?

Nurse I don't know.

Juliet Go and find out, nurse. [*The **Nurse** goes to **Romeo**. **Juliet** speaks to herself*] If he is married, then I fear my grave will be my wedding bed.

Nurse [*Coming back*] His name is Romeo. He's the only son of your enemy, old Montague.

Juliet My only love, sprung from my only hate; seen when unknown, and known too late.

Nurse What's that? What did you say?

Juliet Just a rhyme I learnt from someone I was dancing with just now.

[*Someone calls to **Juliet** from offstage*]

Nurse [*Calling back*] She's coming! [*To **Juliet***] Come along now. They've all gone.

ACT TWO

SCENE 1*

An orchard at the side of Capulet's house.
An upstairs window opens onto a balcony

Romeo
Benvolio
Mercutio

[*Romeo comes in*]

Romeo How can I go, when my heart is here? She is the centre of my world.

[*Benvolio and Mercutio come in. Romeo hides*]

Benvolio Romeo! Cousin Romeo!

Mercutio He's a sensible fellow. He's gone home to bed.

Benvolio No. He came this way, and jumped over that wall. Call him, Mercutio.

Mercutio I'll try a little magic. [*He calls out mockingly*] Romeo! Lover-boy! Madman! Just say two words — "love" and "dove" will do. Speak nicely to my old friend Venus, and her blind brat, Cupid. [*To Benvolio*] He's lying low. I'll raise him up with a spell. [*He calls out*]
By Rosaline's bright eyes,
By her foot, her leg, her thighs, and so on... Appear to us!

Benvolio He'll be furious if he hears you.

Mercutio Oh, I don't think so. It was only a harmless little spell. I'm just using his mistress's charms to rouse him. What *would* make him angry would be if I produced another lover for her.

Benvolio He's hiding among the trees. Lovers are better off in the dark.

Mercutio Yes! Love is blind, after all. [*He calls out*] Oh Romeo, if only your love was a wide open flower, and you were a honey bee! Good night, Romeo. I'm off to bed. This flower bed is too cold for me. [*To Benvolio*] Shall we go?

Benvolio Yes, let's. We'll never find him if he doesn't want us to. [*They go out*]

*The Chorus to Act Two has been omitted.

13

SCENE 2

The same

Romeo
Juliet
Nurse (off stage)

Romeo [*He comes out of his hiding place and speaks to himself*] It's easy for him to laugh; he's not been hurt. [*Juliet comes to the window*] What is that light? It is the east, and Juliet is the sun! Rise, lovely sun, and blot out the cold moon with your warmth and beauty... [*Juliet comes out onto the balcony*] It *is* my lady. Oh, if only she knew she was my love... She seems to be speaking — shall I answer? No, she is talking to the stars; they are asking her to shine in their place. But her eyes are so bright that the birds will think it is dawn, and start singing. Now she is leaning her cheek on her hand. Oh, how I wish I were a glove upon that hand, so that I could touch her cheek.

Juliet [*She sighs*] Oh!

Romeo Oh, speak again bright angel, up there in heaven!

Juliet [*To herself*] Romeo! Romeo! Oh, why are you called "Romeo"? Give up your family and your name! Or else say you love me, and I will give up mine.

Romeo [*To himself*] Shall I speak now?

Juliet [*To herself*] But it's only your name that's my enemy. You'd still be you, even if you were not a Montague. After all, what's in a name? A rose would smell as sweet, whatever we called it; and Romeo would be as perfect whatever his name. Get rid of your name, Romeo. Take me instead.

Romeo [*To himself*] I'll take you at your word. [*Aloud*] Call me your love, and you'll have given me a new name.

Juliet Who's that? Who are you, hiding in the dark, listening to me?

Romeo I don't know how to tell you. I hate my name, because it belongs to your enemy.

Juliet I recognise your voice. Aren't you Romeo, and a Montague?

Romeo Neither, if you don't like them.

Juliet If any of my family find you, they'll kill you. How did you get in?

Romeo Love gave me wings to fly over the wall. Love can do anything. Your family can't stop me.

Juliet If they see you, they'll murder you.

Romeo There's more danger in your eyes than in twenty of their swords. Just smile, and I'll be safe.

Juliet They mustn't find you here.

Romeo The darkness will protect me. Anyway, unless you love me, I'd rather die.

Juliet Who told you how to get here?

Romeo Love did. He and I worked it out together. And for such treasure, I would have sailed to the ends of the earth.

Juliet Oh! You must have heard what I said just now. I feel so ashamed. I wish I could behave sensibly, and take back my words — but I can't... Do you love me? I know you'll say "Yes". And of course I'll believe you. But they say lovers' promises are made to be broken... Oh, gentle Romeo, if you love me, say you will be true to me. But perhaps you think I'm too easily won. If so, I'll frown, and pretend to refuse you. Ah, I fear you *do* think it, sweet Montague. Yet I am too much in love with you to pretend or to flirt. Anyway, you will find me more faithful than those who play hard to get. But if you hadn't overheard me say how much I love you, I would have been more reserved. Please don't think I am giving myself to you lightly.

Romeo Lady, I swear by the silvery light of the moon, which is just...

Juliet No, not by the moon. It's so changeable.

Romeo Then what shall I swear by?

Juliet Don't swear at all. Or, if you must, swear by your own sweet self.

Romeo If you, dear love —

Juliet No, don't swear. Although I rejoice in my love for you, I do not like these promises. They are too rash, too sudden, too like lightning. Our love needs time to grow and blossom. Good night, and sleep well.

Romeo You're not going...!

Juliet What more can I give you?

Romeo Promise to love me.

Juliet But I have already given you my love. I gave it to you even before you asked me. Though I now wish I hadn't.

Romeo But why?

Juliet Because then I could give it to you again! There is no end to my love — the more I give, the more I have to give. [*She hears a noise in her room*] Sh! Someone's coming. Goodbye, my love. [*The **Nurse** calls to her*] Coming, nurse! [*To **Romeo***] Wait there, I'll come out again. [*She goes into her room*]

Romeo O happy night! But perhaps this is all just a dream...

[***Juliet** comes out again*]

Juliet Just three words, Romeo, and then I *will* say goodnight. If you love me truly, and mean to marry me, let me know tomorrow where and when we'll be married. Oh, I will give up all I have and follow you!

Nurse [*From inside*] Miss Juliet!

Juliet [*To the **Nurse***] I'll be in in a minute! [*To **Romeo***] But if you are not serious, please —

Nurse Miss Juliet!

15

Juliet [*To the Nurse*] Just coming, nurse! [*To **Romeo**]* If you are only flirting with me, leave me alone. Leave me to my sorrow... I'll send someone tomorrow.

Romeo I promise —

Juliet Good night, a thousand times. [*She goes in*]

Romeo That means a thousand partings. [*He starts to go*]

[***Juliet** returns*]

Juliet [*She whispers*] Romeo! Romeo! Oh, if only I dared, I'd fill the night with shouts of "Romeo!"

Romeo [*Coming back*] Yes, my angel?

Juliet What time tomorrow?

Romeo By nine o'clock.

Juliet It'll feel like twenty years till then... Now I've forgotten why I called you back!

Romeo I'll wait till you remember.

Juliet Then I'll just go on forgetting, to keep you here.

Romeo Then I'll just stay, so that you'll go on forgetting.

Juliet Oh, it's almost morning, you must go. And yet I wish I had you on a string, like a little bird, so that I could pull you back again.

Romeo I wish you could.

Juliet So do I, my dear. But then I'd smother you with my love... Good night! Good night! I could go on saying that till morning, parting is such sweet sorrow. [*She goes in*]

Romeo May sleep and peace be in your eyes and heart. How I wish I could take their place...! It's almost morning. I must go to Friar Laurence, and tell him my wonderful news, and ask for his help.

SCENE 3

A field near a monastery

| Friar Laurence |
| Romeo |

[***Friar Laurence** comes in carrying a basket*]

Friar Laurence [*He picks herbs as he is speaking*] Well, I must get my basket filled up with these precious herbs, before the sun dries the dew on them. The earth is both cradle and grave to these children of nature, and she feeds them well. Each herb is different, but they all have their uses. It's miraculous, the power that lies buried in them. In fact, every single thing on earth, however vile, can do us some good. On the other hand, there's nothing so perfect that it cannot be misused, then good turns into evil, just as evil can occasionally lead to good. Now, this flower here [*he picks one*] can both kill *and* cure. Its scent revives you, but if you eat it, it will kill you. Man is like that: he contains both good and evil. And if the evil is too strong, it destroys him.

[***Romeo** comes in*]

Romeo Good morning, Father.

Friar Bless my soul! Who can this be? [*He sees **Romeo***] Well, young man, you're up early. What's the matter? Old men may be kept awake by their worries, but young men should sleep soundly. Or perhaps you haven't been to bed at all!

Romeo You're right, I haven't been to bed. I was somewhere much nicer.

Friar May God forgive you! Were you with Rosaline?

Romeo With Rosaline? Oh, no. I've forgotten all that.

Friar That's my good boy. Where have you been, then?

Romeo I'll tell you. I was at a party at my enemy's house, when — suddenly — I was hurt by someone whom I myself had hurt. The cure for both of us lies in your help and blessing.

Friar How can I help you if you speak in riddles, young man? Say what you mean.

Romeo Very well. I am in love with rich Capulet's beautiful daughter, and she loves me. All that remains to be done is for you to marry us. I'll tell you when and how we met as we go along. But promise me you will marry us today!

Friar By Saint Francis, what a change! Is Rosaline, whom you loved so dearly, forgotten already? It seems that young men love with their eyes and not with their hearts. Good Lord! When I think of all the salt water that has run down your cheeks. What a waste! Huh! I can still see an old tear stain on your cheek and hear your groans for Rosaline. And now you've changed your tune, eh? Repeat after me: "When men are so weak, what can we expect of women?"

Romeo But you used to tell me off for loving Rosaline.

Friar Not for loving her, young man. For being infatuated.

Romeo And you told me to bury my love.

Friar Yes, but not to dig another one up.

Romeo Please don't tell me off. The girl I love now loves me in return. The other didn't.

Friar The other one knew perfectly well you didn't mean what you said. Come along, young butterfly, come with me. I'll help you, but only because a happy marriage may bring the Montagues and Capulets together, and turn their hatred into love.

Romeo Come on! Let's go.

Friar Now, now! Remember: more haste, less speed.

17

SCENE 4

A street in Verona

| Mercutio |
| Benvolio |
| Romeo |
| Nurse |
| Peter |

[*Mercutio and Benvolio come in*]

Mercutio Where the devil has Romeo got to? Didn't he go home last night?

Benvolio No — according to his servant.

Mercutio If that Rosaline doesn't stop tormenting him, he'll go mad.

Benvolio Tybalt, Capulet's nephew, has sent him a letter.

Mercutio I bet it's a challenge.

Benvolio And Romeo is sure to answer it.

Mercutio No, he won't! Poor old Romeo is dead, stabbed in the eye by a woman's looks, pierced through the ear by a love song, shot through the heart by Cupid! He isn't fit to face Tybalt.

Benvolio Huh! Tybalt!

Mercutio Tybalt's a foxy fellow, I tell you, a real cool customer. He fights in strict time, as if he's a conductor: one, two, three, [*he makes gestures*] and the fourth goes straight for you, and cuts off your shirt button! He was trained at the top college, you know, where he learnt the fatal *passado*, the *punto reverso*, the *hay*!*

Benvolio The what?

Mercutio The devil take these ridiculous show-offs, with their silly voices. [*In a posh accent*] "He's a jolly good chap! He's jolly brave, what! He's a jolly bad lot!" What is the world coming to, grandad, when we have to put up with these smart layabouts. To be in fashion, they have to wear such tight trousers they can't even sit down. They have to stand on ceremony!

Benvolio Here comes Romeo!

Mercutio Without his roe, like a dried herring! Has flesh ever been so fishified? Soon he'll be writing poetry to his Rosaline, and saying that she is heavenlier than Helen and sweeter than Rita. [*Romeo comes in*] *Bonjour*, Signor Romeo! You certainly gave us the petticoat last night.

Romeo Good morning. What do you mean, "the petticoat"?

Mercutio The slip, sir! You gave us the slip. Don't you see?

Romeo [*He groans*] I'm sorry, Mercutio, but my business was urgent. I had to be excused.

---

*Sword strokes in fencing

18

Mercutio All right, one to you!

Romeo That's very sweet of you.

Mercutio That's because I've been prettily brought up.

Romeo Pretty, like a flower.

Mercutio That's right.

Romeo Do you know, my shoes are rather pretty.

Mercutio Well then, see if you can follow this: my wit will outlast your feeble little sole.

Romeo Upon my soul, a very feeble little joke!

Mercutio Help, Benvolio! I'm at my wits' end.

Romeo Then I've won!

Mercutio If it's a wild goose chase, I've had it, because you're a real goose. Got you there!

Romeo You always play the fool, you silly goose.

Mercutio Watch it! You might strain your little brain.

Romeo And an injured bird is a dead duck!

Mercutio Isn't this better than groaning for love? This is more like it, Romeo. This is the real you, the wholesome, natural you. That thing called "love" is like a blubbering idiot, running up and down, looking for somewhere to hide his toy.

Benvolio Stop it, you two.

Mercutio I can't stop now, not at the goal mouth.

Romeo Here's some fun! [*He points off stage*] A sail! A sail!

Mercutio Two sales — one in the shirt, and another in the skirt department!

[*The **Nurse** and **Peter** come in*]

Nurse My fan, Peter!

Mercutio [*To **Peter***] Give it to her, Peter. I don't *fan*cy her face. [***Peter** gives the **Nurse** her fan*]

Nurse Good morning, gentlemen.

Mercutio Good afternoon, good lady.

Nurse Is it afternoon?

Mercutio The hands of the clock are both up. [*He makes a rude gesture*]

Nurse How dare you! What sort of a creature are you?

Romeo Made by God, Madam, but marred by himself.

Nurse "Marred by himself", eh? Mmm. I like that...! Gentlemen, can you tell me where I can find young Romeo?

Romeo Yes, I can. And I can also tell you that by the time you've found him, young Romeo will be older than when you asked for him... I am the youngest of that name, for want of a -er- worse.

Nurse That's good!

Mercutio [*To the Nurse*] What? Is "worse" good?

Nurse [*To Romeo*] If you are Romeo, sir, I would depreciate a word with you. [*Romeo goes to one side with the Nurse*]

Benvolio Aha! She's going to excite him to supper.

Mercutio [*Pretending to laugh*] Haw! Haw! Whore!

Romeo [*To Mercutio*] What have you found now?

Mercutio Not a cow, sir; not even a purple cow in a vegetarian pie, that's a bit past it. [*He sings*]
> I never saw a purple cow,
> I never hope to see one;
> But I can tell you, anyhow,
> I'd rather see than be one!

Romeo, let's meet at your father's house, and have dinner there.

Romeo All right, I'll see you there.

Mercutio [*To the Nurse*] Goodbye, old thing! [*Mercutio and Benvolio go out*]

Nurse Excuse me, sir; who is that imprudent fellow?

Romeo He's a man who loves the sound of his own voice. He'll say more in a minute than he'll do in a month.

Nurse If he's rude to me, I'll sit on him — however cocky he is. And if I can't deal with him myself, I'll find those who can. Cheeky rascal! Who does he think I am? One of his fancy girls? [*To Peter*] And all you do is stand there, and let people indulge my honour!

Peter I never saw anyone indulge you! If I had, I'd have got my weapon out in a flash. That is, if I thought there was a chance of a good quarrel, and the law was on my side.

Nurse Oh, I'm so cross, I'm shaking all over, like a jelly. Cheeky devil! [*To Romeo*] Now, sir, as I was saying, my young lady asked me to find you and give you a message, but I'm not going to tell you what she said. I'll keep that to myself. But let me tell you this, young man. If you are just leading her up the garden path, as they say, I call it shameful, for my lady is very young. It would be a really disgraceful thing to do to any young lady.

Romeo Nurse, please give my best wishes to your mistress. I promise I'll —

Nurse Oh, my dear sir, I'll tell her. She'll be so happy!

Romeo But, nurse, I haven't said anything yet. What will you tell her?

Nurse I'll tell her that you've promised. I can see you're a gentleman.

Romeo Tell her to find an excuse for coming to church this afternoon. We'll be married by Friar Laurence. Here, take this. [*He offers her some money*]

Nurse Oh no, sir. I really couldn't...

Romeo Go on, take it.

Nurse [*She takes the money*] This afternoon, sir. She'll be there.

Romeo And, nurse, meet my servant behind the abbey wall in an hour's time. He'll bring you a rope ladder, which I'll use to climb to my love tonight. Goodbye. Keep your word, and I'll pay you well. Goodbye. Remember me to your mistress. [*He starts to go*]

Nurse God bless you! Just a moment, sir!

Romeo [*He comes back*] What is it, nurse?

Nurse Can we trust your man? You know what they say: two can keep a secret better than three.

Romeo You can depend on him, nurse.

Nurse Well, sir, my mistress is the sweetest lady. Lordy, I remember her when she was a little chattering thing… By the way, there's a nobleman in town, called Paris, who's after her. I tease her, sometimes, and tell her that Paris is the better man — but, do you know, she goes as white as a sheet when I say that… Don't "rosemary" and "Romeo" both begin with the same letter?

Romeo Yes, nurse. Why? They both begin with "r"s.

Nurse Don't tease me, sir. "R"s, indeed! I'm sure it's some other letter. Anyway, she made up such a pretty ditty with it, it would have done you good to hear it.

Romeo Give her my love. [*He goes out*]

Nurse I will, I will. [*She calls*] Peter!

Peter Coming!

Nurse [*To Peter*] Come along! Lead the way!

SCENE 5

Capulet's garden

| Juliet |
| Nurse |
| (Peter) |

[*Juliet comes in*]

Juliet It was nine o'clock when I sent nurse to him, and she promised to come back in half an hour. Perhaps she hasn't been able to see him! No, that can't be it. Of course, I'd forgotten: she's lame. Love's messengers should be thoughts, which fly ten times faster than light… Oh, if only she was young and in love. But these old people, they behave as if they're already dead, they are so heavy and slow. Ah, here she comes! [*Nurse and Peter come in*] Sweet nurse, what news? Did you see him? Send your servant away.

Nurse [*To Peter*] Peter, wait at the gate. [*Peter goes out*]

Juliet Now, good, sweet nurse... Oh Lord! Why are you looking so sad? Even if your news is bad, tell it cheerfully. And if it's good news, you shouldn't look so sour.

Nurse I'm tired, let me rest a bit. Oh, how my bones ache! What a trip I've had.

Juliet I wish you had my bones and I had your news. Please, nurse, tell me.

Nurse What's the hurry? Can't you see I'm out of breath?

Juliet How can you be out of breath, when you've got enough breath to *say* you're out of breath? Your excuses are longer than your message. Just tell me — is it good or bad?

Nurse Well, I must say, you *have* made a silly choice. Fancy picking Romeo! He may have the most handsome face in the world, but the rest of him is... perfect! His manners are appalling... but he's as gentle as a lamb. But enough of that! Have you had your dinner yet?

Juliet No. But I knew all this before. What did he say about our marriage?

Nurse Oh, my head. I've got a splitting headache! My back! [*Juliet rubs her back*] No, the other side... Shame on you, sending me traipsing up and down like this. You'll be the death of me.

Juliet I'm sorry you're not well. Sweet, sweet nurse, tell me what my love said.

Nurse Your love is a kind, polite and handsome gentleman, and he says — where's your mother?

Juliet Where's my mother? She's in the house, of course. Where else should she be? What a strange thing to say: "Your love is a kind gentleman, and he says, 'Where's your mother?'"

Nurse My goodness, young lady, you *are* impatient! Is this the way to treat my aching bones? In future, you can carry your own messages.

Juliet Oh, come on, nurse! Please, what did Romeo say?

Nurse Have you got permission to go to confession today?

Juliet Yes.

Nurse Well then, go to Friar Laurence. You'll find a husband there, waiting to make you into a wife. Look at you! It doesn't take much to make you blush, does it! Hurry along to church. I must go and fetch a ladder, so that your love can climb to your nest when it's dark. I'm doing all the work now, but it'll be your turn tonight! I'll go in to dinner, while you get along to Friar Laurence.

Juliet Oh, how lucky I am! Goodbye, dear nurse.

[*They go out opposite ways*]

SCENE 6

Friar Laurence's room

[*Friar Laurence and Romeo come in*]

Friar God bless this marriage, and may we never live to regret it.

Romeo Whatever sorrow the future may bring, it can never outweigh the joy of one short minute with her. Just join our hands in marriage, father, and let death — that kill-joy — do his worst. It will be enough just to call her mine.

Friar Such burning passion will burn itself out; a calm and gentle love is more likely to last. Slow and steady... Here she comes! [*Juliet comes running in and kisses Romeo*] Her step is so light, she'll never wear these stones out. Yes, lovers can walk on spiders' webs and never break them. Of such airy nothings are the pleasures of this world made.

Juliet Good evening, father. [*She kisses him*]

Friar Romeo can greet you for me.

[*Romeo kisses Juliet twice*]

Juliet That's one too many. I must give you one back. [*She kisses him*]

Romeo Dear Juliet, if your joy is as great as mine, and you can describe it better, use your sweet voice to tell the world of our happiness.

Juliet It is what we feel that matters, not the words we use. Those who can count their wealth are beggars. My love is too great to be measured.

Friar Come along, we'd better get the knot tied quickly. I shan't leave you two alone until you are married!

ACT THREE

SCENE 1

A street in Verona

Benvolio	Citizen
Mercutio	(Other citizens)
(Their friends)	Prince Escalus
Mercutio's servant	Montague
Tybalt	(Lady Montague)
His friend	(Capulet)
(His other friends)	Lady Capulet
Romeo	(Their friends)

[*Benvolio, Mercutio, his Servant, and some of their Friends come in*]

Benvolio Come on, Mercutio, let's go. There are Capulets around. There's sure to be a fight if we run into them. Tempers get pretty high in this heat.

Mercutio You know, you're the kind of fellow who goes into a pub, bangs his sword down on a table, says, "I hope to God I shan't need to use this", and by the time he has had a couple of drinks, he's attacking the barman.

Benvolio Am I like that?

Mercutio Oh, come on, you know you are. You've got the hottest temper in Italy.

Benvolio That's a good one!

Mercutio One's enough. If there were two like you, we'd soon have neither; you'd have killed each other. I know you. You'd quarrel with a man for having a hair more or less in his beard than you have. You'd pick a quarrel with a man for cracking hazel nuts, just because your eyes are hazel-coloured. Your head is as full of quarrels as a stuffed egg, and as rotten. Didn't you once quarrel with a man for coughing and waking up your dog that was sleeping in the sun? And then you lecture me about quarrelling!

Benvolio If I was as ready to quarrel as you are, I'd be dead and gone in an hour.

Mercutio You're gone in the head already!

Benvolio Uh-uh... Here come the Capulets!

Mercutio Why the devil should I care?

[*Tybalt comes in with some Friends*]

Tybalt [*To his Friends*] Stay close to me, I'm going to speak to them. [*To Benvolio and Mercutio*] Good afternoon, gentlemen. I'd like a word with one of you.

Mercutio Only *one* word, with *one* of us? Make it a word and a blow.

Tybalt Just give me an excuse. I'm ready.

Mercutio Can't you find one for yourself?

Tybalt Mercutio, aren't you one of Romeo's band?

24

Mercutio Band? So you're turning us into musicians, are you? Then prepare yourself for some deadly discords! Look — here's my fiddlestick. [*He draws his sword*] This'll make you dance. Romeo's band, indeed!

Benvolio [*To Mercutio*] It's too public here. Go somewhere private, or talk sensibly here, or else just go. Everyone can see us here.

Mercutio Eyes were made for seeing. Let them look! I shan't budge an inch, not for anyone!

Tybalt [*He sees Romeo coming*] Ah! Here comes my man.

Mercutio Your man, indeed! But if it's a fight you are wanting, he's certainly your man... [*He bows mockingly*] Sir!

[*Romeo comes in*]

Tybalt Romeo, you are a villain!

Romeo Tybalt, I have my reasons for not getting angry with you. I am no villain, so goodbye. I can see you don't understand. [*Romeo starts going*]

Tybalt You won't get out of it that easily, boy. Turn round, and draw your sword.

Romeo I never hurt you. In fact, I love you better than you can imagine, and you will soon know why. Be satisfied, good Capulet. Your name is as dear to me as my own.

Mercutio Shame on you, Romeo, you coward! Tybalt, you ratcatcher, come with me.

Tybalt What do *you* want?

Mercutio Just one of your nine lives, King of cats! And when I've dealt with that one, we'll see about the rest. Come on, pull your sword out, before I push mine in!

Tybalt Right! [*He draws his sword*]

Romeo Please, Mercutio, put your sword away.

Mercutio [*To Tybalt*] Come sir. Let's see your famous "passado"! [*He fights with Tybalt*]

Romeo Stop them, Benvolio! [*To Tybalt and Mercutio*] Shame on you, gentlemen! Tybalt! Mercutio! You know the Prince has strictly forbidden fighting in Verona. Stop, Tybalt! My dear Mercutio! [*Romeo gets in between Tybalt and Mercutio to try and stop them fighting, so Mercutio does not see a thrust from Tybalt, which wounds him in the chest*]

One of Tybalt's friends Come along, Tybalt. [*Tybalt goes out with his Friends*]

Mercutio I'm hurt. A plague on both your houses! Oh, I'm done for. Has he got away?

Benvolio Has he hurt you?

Mercutio Yes, a scratch, but it's enough. [*To his Servant*] Boy, go and fetch a doctor. [*The Servant goes out*]

Romeo Take heart, man, it can't be too bad.

Mercutio It's not as deep as a well, or as wide as a church door, but it's enough, it'll do. I'll be a grave man tomorrow! I'm finished, I tell you. A plague on both your houses! To be scratched to death by a rat, a mouse, a cat! By a villain who fights "one-two" by the book. Why the devil did you get between us, Romeo?

Romeo I was only trying to help.

Mercutio Help me into a house, Benvolio, or I shall faint. The devil take both your families! They've made worms' meat out of me. I'm done for. You and your families... [*Benvolio helps him out*]

Romeo [*To himself*] So Mercutio — my dearest friend and the Prince's close relation — has been fatally wounded, for defending my honour after Tybalt had insulted me: Tybalt, who only an hour ago became my cousin. Oh, sweet Juliet, your beauty has made me effeminate, and turned me into a coward.

[*Benvolio comes in*]

Benvolio O Romeo, brave Mercutio is dead. He was too gallant for this world.

Romeo I fear this tragedy is only the beginning...

Benvolio Here comes that firebrand Tybalt again.

Romeo Yes, in triumph, while Mercutio lies dead. Goodbye, gentleness! Anger shall guide me now! [*Tybalt comes in*] Right, Tybalt! Take back your insult. Mercutio's soul is waiting for yours to keep it company. Either you, or I, or both of us, must join him.

Tybalt You were his friend, you wretched boy! *You* shall join him.

Romeo [*Drawing his sword*] This will settle it. [*They fight, and **Romeo** kills **Tybalt***]

Benvolio Go, Romeo! Quick! There are people around. You've killed him. Don't just stand there! The Prince will have you put to death if you're caught. Quick — go!

Romeo Oh, I am fortune's fool!

Benvolio What are you waiting for?

[*Romeo goes out. Some Citizens come in*]

Citizen Where's that murderer Tybalt? Which way did he go?

Benvolio Tybalt? [*He points*] There he is.

[*Prince Escalus comes in with Montague, Lady Montague, Capulet, Lady Capulet and some of their Friends*]

Prince Where are the wretches who started this?

Benvolio I can explain what happened, noble Prince. [*He points at Tybalt*] There lies the man who killed your nephew Mercutio. Romeo killed him.

Lady Capulet [*She goes to Tybalt*] Tybalt! Oh, my brother's child. He's dead! Oh husband! Prince, you must make the Montagues pay for this with their blood. Oh nephew, nephew!

Prince [*To Benvolio*] Who started this bloodshed?

Benvolio Tybalt, sir. Romeo asked him, very courteously, to consider how trivial the quarrel was, and how upset you would be. He spoke gently and calmly, but Tybalt refused to listen, and attacked Mercutio, who fought back fiercely. Romeo tried to stop them, and rushed in between them. But a vicious thrust from Tybalt fatally wounded brave Mercutio. Tybalt then fled, but he came back later, looking for Romeo, who by now was determined to get his revenge, and the two of them went at each other. Before I could separate them, Tybalt was dead. Then Romeo turned and fled. That's the truth, I promise you.

Lady Capulet [*To the Prince*] He's a Montague. You can't trust him. There must have been at least twenty of them against Tybalt. I demand justice! Romeo killed Tybalt, so Romeo must die.

Prince Yes, Romeo killed Tybalt. But then, Tybalt had already killed Mercutio. Who is to pay for Mercutio's death?

Montague Not Romeo, Prince. He was Mercutio's friend. He only did what the law would have done.

Prince And for that, I banish him from Verona. One of my own family has died because of your barbaric quarrel, and I'll make you pay heavily for that. No! Nothing you can say will make me alter my verdict. Romeo must leave Verona immediately. If he is ever found here, he will be put to death. We cannot afford to pardon murderers. [*He points at Tybalt*] Take him away.

SCENE 2

A room in Capulet's house

| Juliet |
| Nurse |

[*Juliet comes in*]

Juliet Oh sun, set quickly, and bring in dark night, so that Romeo can steal into these arms. Lovers have no need of light: their own beauty is enough. Or, if it is true that love is blind, then darkness suits it best. Come, gentle night! Show me how to win my love by giving myself to him, and hide my blushes till my love grows bold. When love is true, then love is innocent. Come, night. Come, Romeo, and lighten this dark night. And when I die, take him, and cut him out in little stars, so that all the world will be in love with night... I am married, and yet not a wife. How the time drags! I feel like a child who has been given new clothes, but is not allowed to wear them... Here comes my nurse! [*The Nurse comes in looking very unhappy. She is carrying a rope ladder*] What's the news, nurse? What have you got there? Is it the ladder?

Nurse Yes, yes, the ladder. [*She throws it on the floor*]

Juliet What's the matter?

27

Nurse Alas, he's dead. It's all over with us, lady. It's all over. He's gone, he's killed, he's dead.

Juliet Can heaven be so cruel?

Nurse Romeo can, even if heaven can't. O Romeo! Who would have thought it of you?

Juliet What kind of devil are you, to torment me like this? Such torture belongs in hell, not here. Has Romeo killed himself? If you say "Yes", that one short sound will seal my fate, as surely as deadly poison.

Nurse Oh, I saw the wound with my own eyes, here on his chest. His body, so pale and pitiful, covered in blood — I fainted at the sight.

Juliet Break, my poor heart, break; eyes, go blind. Let my wretched body return to earth, and lie with Romeo in one grave.

Nurse O Tybalt! Gentle, honest Tybalt! The best friend I ever had. That I should live to see you dead!

Juliet What kind of a storm is this, that blows first one way, then the other? Is my cousin Tybalt dead, and my dearest husband Romeo killed? Is this the Day of Judgement? Who is there left alive, if these two are dead?

Nurse Tybalt is dead; and Romeo, who killed him, is banished.

Juliet Oh God! Did Romeo's hand shed Tybalt's blood?

Nurse Alas, it did!

Juliet How could such a beautiful face hide such evil? How can a devil look so like an angel?

Nurse Men can't be trusted. They're all liars — every one of them. Where's Peter? Give me some brandy. These sorrows make me old. Shame come to Romeo!

Juliet Curse your tongue for saying such a thing! Romeo was born for honour, not for shame. What a beast I was to be angry with him.

Nurse How can you speak well of the man who killed your cousin?

Juliet Shall I speak ill of the man who is my husband? Oh, my poor Romeo! If I, your wife for just three hours, can be so cruel, who will speak well of you? But why, you wicked man, did you kill my cousin? Because, otherwise, that wicked cousin would have killed you. Stop crying, silly girl. Tears are for sorrow, not joy. My husband is alive, whom Tybalt would have killed. All this is comfort, so why am I weeping? Ah! There is a word far more terrible than death. The memory of it presses on me like a guilty conscience. A word I long to forget, but cannot: "banished". That one word is worse than a thousand deaths. Tybalt's death would have been sorrow enough, but to say "Romeo is banished" is to kill father, mother, Tybalt, Romeo, and Juliet — to kill them all. There's no limit to the horror in that word... Where are my father and mother, nurse?

Nurse Weeping and wailing over Tybalt's body. I'll take you to them.

Juliet Long after their tears for Tybalt are dry, I will still be weeping over Romeo's banishment. [*She looks at the rope ladder*] Poor ropes, you have been cheated. He made you as a highway to my bed, but I must die a virgin and a widow. Come nurse, I'll go to my wedding bed, where death, not Romeo shall be my partner.

Nurse Go to your room. I'll find Romeo to comfort you. I know where he is. Listen! Your Romeo will be here tonight. He's hiding at Friar Laurence's.

Juliet Yes, go to him. [*She gives the **Nurse** a ring*] Give this to my true love, and tell him to come and say his last goodbye.

SCENE 3
Friar Laurence's room

| Friar Laurence |
| Romeo |
| Nurse |

[***Friar Laurence** comes in*]

Friar Come here, Romeo! You poor creature, you seem to be married to disaster...

[***Romeo** comes in*]

Romeo What news, father? What is the Prince's verdict?

Friar He has been kind. His verdict is not death, but banishment.

Romeo Banishment? Oh, be merciful, and say "death". Banishment has far more terror for me than death.

Friar You are banished from Verona. But be patient, the world is large.

Romeo There is no world for me outside Verona — only torture and hell. To be banished is to be banished from the world, and that is death. You are just playing with words. Calling death banishment is like cutting off my head with a golden axe, and smiling while you do it.

Friar Wicked, ungrateful boy! According to our law, you should be sentenced to death, but the kind Prince has changed it to banishment. Can't you see how merciful he is?

Romeo It's torture, not mercy. Heaven is here, where Juliet lives, where every cat and dog may look at her, but not Romeo. Why, the very flies in Verona have more rights than Romeo has. And you say that exile is not death? Have you no other way to kill me, some quick and brutal way? Some poison, or a knife? Banished! Oh, Father, that is a word the damned use in hell. How can you, a holy priest who calls himself my friend, find it in your heart to crush me with it?

Friar Listen to me, you crazy fellow.

Romeo You'll only talk about banishment again.

Friar I'll teach you how to bear your banishment.

Romeo That word again! Forget your teaching. It's useless, unless you can teach me how to make a Juliet, transplant a town, or reverse a Prince's verdict. Don't speak to me.

Friar Well, it seems that madmen have no ears!

Romeo Is that surprising, when wise men have no eyes?

Friar Let's discuss it, Romeo.

Romeo How can you talk about things you don't understand? If you were my age, married to Juliet just an hour ago, with Tybalt dead — loving her as I do and banished like me — then you could talk. You'd tear your hair and fall upon the ground. [*He throws himself on the floor. There is a knock on the door*]

Friar Get up. There's someone at the door. Go and hide.

Romeo No, I shan't. [*More knocking*]

Friar What a noise! Who's there? [*To **Romeo**] Get up, Romeo. You'll be caught. [*Calling*] Coming! [*To **Romeo**] Get up and go to my study. This is stupid! [*More knocking. He calls out*] All right, all right, I'm coming! [*He goes to the door*] Who is it? What do you want?

Nurse [*Outside*] Let me in, and I'll tell you. I'm from Lady Juliet.

Friar Welcome, then. [*He opens the door and the **Nurse** comes in*]

Nurse Oh Friar Laurence, where's my lady's husband, where's Romeo?

Friar There he is! Drunk on his own tears!

Nurse That's exactly how my mistress is. She just lies there, weeping and wailing. What a sad business! [*To **Romeo**] Stand up, if you're a man. For Juliet's sake, pull yourself together.

Romeo Did you say "Juliet"? How is my lady? Does she call me a murderer for having killed our new-found joy? Where is she? How is she? And what does she say about our hopeless love?

Nurse She says nothing, sir, but weeps, and weeps, and falls upon her bed, and gets up, and calls for Tybalt, and cries out against Romeo.

Romeo As if the sound of that name had murdered her, just as I have murdered her cousin, Tybalt! Oh Friar, where in this horrible body of mine can I find my name? Tell me, so that I can tear it out. [*He tries to stab himself with his dagger, but the **Friar** stops him*]

Friar Stop! You look like a man, but you are crying like a woman, and behaving like a wild animal. I am amazed at you! By Saint Francis, I thought you had more sense. You have killed Tybalt. Are you now trying to kill yourself? And destroy the lady that lives for you? Why do you curse your fate, when fate has been so kind to you? Look at you: you're handsome, loving, and intelligent, but you misuse your gifts. Come on! Think how fortunate you are. Your Juliet is alive. Tybalt would have killed you, but you killed him — in that, too, you are fortunate. The law has been kind to you. Fortune has showered you with blessings, but you are behaving like a spoilt and sulky child. I warn you, that way lies misery... Go to your love, as we planned, and comfort her. But leave before the city gates are closed, or you won't be able to get out. Then go to Mantua. Stay there until we can announce your marriage, reconcile your two families, ask the Prince for pardon, and call you back joyfully. [*To the Nurse*] You go first, nurse. Give my greetings to your lady, and make sure that everyone gets to bed early. Romeo will follow.

Nurse I could stay here all night, listening to your good advice. What a marvellous thing education is...! [*To Romeo*] Sir, I'll tell my lady you are coming. [*She starts to go, then turns back and gives him the ring*] She told me to give you this ring, sir. Don't be long, it's getting late. [*She goes out*]

Romeo [*Looking at the ring*] How this comforts me...

Friar You must go. Leave Verona before the gates are locked, or go at dawn in a disguise. Remain in Mantua. I'll send you news through your servant. [*They shake hands*] It's late. Goodbye. Goodnight.

Romeo I'm sorry to leave so hastily, but my Juliet calls me. Goodbye!

<table>
<tr><td rowspan="2">SCENE 4
A room in Capulet's house</td><td>Capulet</td></tr>
<tr><td>(Lady Capulet)
Paris</td></tr>
</table>

[*Capulet, Lady Capulet and Paris come in*]

Capulet Because of all this trouble, I haven't had time to talk to my daughter. She was very fond of her cousin Tybalt, and so was I. Well, death comes to us all... It's late — she won't come down tonight. I should really be in bed myself.

Paris Yes, this is hardly the time for courting. [*To Lady Capulet*] Good night, madam. Please remember me to your daughter.

[*Paris starts to go, but Capulet calls him back*]

Capulet Sir! I will offer you my daughter's hand, since I think she will obey me. In fact, I know she will. [*To Lady Capulet*] Wife, go and see her before you go to bed. Tell her — are you listening? — that my son Paris loves her, and that next Wednesday... Wait, what's the day today?

Paris Monday, sir.

Capulet Monday. Hmm. Then Wednesday is too soon. Let it be Thursday. [*To Lady Capulet*] Tell her she'll be married to Count Paris on Thursday. Can you be ready? We'll just have a few friends, otherwise people may think we're being disrespectful to our nephew Tybalt. [*To Paris*] What do you say to Thursday?

Paris I wish Thursday was tomorrow.

Capulet Off you go, then. Thursday it is. [*To Lady Capulet*] Go to Juliet before you go to bed, and tell her the marriage will be on Thursday. [*To Paris*] Good night, my lord. [*Paris goes out. Capulet calls to his servants*] Bring me a light! It's so late, we'll soon be able to call it early!

31

Romeo
Juliet
Nurse (Off stage)
—
Lady Capulet
Juliet
Capulet
Nurse

SCENE 5

The balcony outside the window of Juliet's bedroom,
then Juliet's bedroom

[*Romeo and Juliet come onto the balcony. The rope ladder is hanging from it*]

Juliet Must you be gone? It's not nearly dawn. That was a nightingale you heard, not the morning lark. It sings in that tree every night. Believe me, my love, it *was* a nightingale.

Romeo It is the lark, telling us it is morning, not a nightingale. Look, my love, the light is in the east, the stars are fading, it's almost day. I must go — if I stay, I shall die.

Juliet I'm sure that's not daylight. It's some meteor from the sun, sent to light you on your way to Mantua. You don't need to go yet. Please stay.

Romeo Then let them catch me, let them put me to death, if that's what you want. I'll say that that is not the dawn, but the pale light of the crescent moon; and that it's not the lark singing so high above us. I'd much rather stay than go. If Juliet wishes it, I will welcome death... [*Cheerfully*] Let's talk. It's not day yet.

Juliet Oh yes, it is, it is! You must go. It *is* the lark singing so out of tune. They say her song is sweet, but that can't be true, because her voice divides us. Now you *must* go. It's getting lighter all the time.

Romeo Yes, but our future grows darker.

[*The Nurse calls from Juliet's bedroom*]

Nurse Madam!

Juliet Yes, nurse?

Nurse Your mother's coming! It's morning! Look out!

Juliet So the day comes in, and life goes out.

Romeo Goodbye! Goodbye! [*He kisses her, and goes down the ladder*]

Juliet So you are gone. Oh, my lover, my husband, my friend! I must hear from you every day. Each minute will seem like a year: I shall be old before I see my Romeo again!

Romeo Goodbye! I will send my greetings to you as often as I can, my love.

Juliet Do you think we shall ever meet again?

Romeo Of course we will. And one day, in years to come, we'll *enjoy* talking about these troubles.

Juliet Oh God! I have a sense of something terrible... You look to me, down there, as if you were in a tomb. You look so pale!

32

Romeo And so do you, my love — pale with sorrow. Goodbye! Goodbye!
[*He goes out*]

Juliet Oh Fortune, be your fickle self, and send my faithful Romeo back to me soon.

Lady Capulet [*From Juliet's bedroom*] Hello, daughter. Are you up?

Juliet [*To herself*] It's my mother! Why is she up so early? I wonder what she wants. [*She goes into her bedroom*]
[*The scene now changes to Juliet's bedroom*]

Lady Capulet How are you Juliet?

Juliet I don't feel well, mother.

Lady Capulet Still mourning for your cousin's death? You can't bring him back to life, so stop crying. It's silly to go on and on.

Juliet But I must mourn for my friend.

Lady Capulet I think you are crying because the villain who murdered him is still alive.

Juliet What villain, mother?

Lady Capulet That wicked Romeo.

Juliet [*To herself*] He's anything but wicked, God forgive him! I certainly do, with all my heart. [*To her mother*] He causes me more sorrow than anyone.

Lady Capulet Yes, because he is still alive, the murderer.

Juliet And out of reach of these hands.

Lady Capulet Don't worry, we'll have our revenge! I'll get someone in Mantua to poison him, so that he'll join Tybalt and you'll be satisfied.

Juliet I shall never be satisfied until I see Romeo — dead. Mother, if you can find a man to take a poison to him, I'll prepare something that will go straight to his heart. How I hate hearing his name without being able to go to him and repay him for what has happened!

Lady Capulet You find the poison, and I'll find the man... But now I have some good news for you, girl.

Juliet We can do with some good news, mother.

Lady Capulet You have a good and caring father, child, and to take your mind off your sorrows, he has arranged something special and unexpected. Early next Thursday morning, that young gentleman, Count Paris, will make you a happy bride at Saint Peter's church.

Juliet By Saint Peter, he will do no such thing! I am amazed at this hurry. Am I to be married even before I've been courted? Please tell my father that I will not marry — yet. And when I do, it will be to Romeo — whom you know I hate — rather than to Paris. Good news indeed!

Lady Capulet Here comes your father. Tell him so yourself, and see how he takes it!

[*Capulet* and the **Nurse** come in]

Capulet At sunset, the earth is wet with dew; but now my brother's son is dead, it pours with rain. What? Still spouting like a fountain, girl? All this sighing and crying is like a storm at sea. Unless there's a calm, your body will sink like a boat. [*To* **Lady Capulet**] Well, wife, have you told her about my decision?

Lady Capulet Yes. She thanks you, and says "No". I wish the little fool was married to her grave!

Capulet What? Do I hear you correctly, wife? She says "No"? Doesn't she feel proud? Isn't she grateful to us for having found her such a splendid husband?

Juliet Not proud. But I *am* grateful, father. I can never be proud of what I hate, but I do thank you, because you meant well.

Capulet What's all this? Playing with words, are you? Not "proud", but "grateful"? Don't you "grateful" me, young lady. Get yourself ready to go with Paris to Saint Peter's church next Thursday, or I'll drag you there myself. Don't just sit there looking pale and ill. Get on with it! [*He slaps her*]

Lady Capulet Stop that! [*She pulls him back*] Shame on you! Are you mad?

Juliet [*She kneels*] Please, father, I beg you, listen —

Capulet Be quiet, you disobedient wretch! You'll go to church on Thursday, or never look me in the face again. No. Don't speak. Don't say a word. My fingers itch...! [*He raises his hand*] Wife, to think that we wished God had blessed us with more than one child. Huh! I now see that this one was one too many, and that we were cursed, not blessed. Out of my sight, shameless hussy!

Nurse Poor child! Sir, you are wrong to scold her like this.

Capulet What's that? Hold your tongue, my good woman!

Nurse Can't I even say —

Capulet Quiet, you mumbling fool! Go and take your good advice to the kitchen. We don't need it here.

Lady Capulet [*To* **Capulet**] Calm down! Calm down!

Capulet God! It makes me mad! I work day and night to get her a husband, and now that I've found one — a rich and handsome young man from a good family, as fine a man as one could hope for — she whines and whimpers, and says, "I won't marry, I can't love, I'm too young, please excuse me". Excuse you, indeed! I'll send you packing, young lady, if you don't marry. Go where you like. You shan't live in this house with me. Think about it. I'm not joking. Thursday's almost here. If you are my child, I'll marry you to my friend. If not, go hang, beg, starve, die in the streets. I swear I'll never call you "daughter" again. I mean it. I shan't break my word. [*He goes out*]

34

Juliet Is there no pity in heaven for my grief? Sweet mother, don't turn me away. Put off this marriage for a month, or even a week. Otherwise, prepare my wedding bed in that dark tomb where Tybalt lies.

Lady Capulet I've nothing more to say to you. Do what you like. [*She goes out*]

Juliet How can we stop this, nurse? My husband is alive: my marriage vows cannot be cancelled. Comfort me — tell me what to do. Oh God! To think that heaven should play such mean tricks on someone as weak as I. [*Pause*] Can't you give me some comfort, nurse?

Nurse This is what I say. Romeo is banished, and it's a million to one he'll never dare to come back and claim you as his wife. Or if he did, it would have to be secretly. So, things being what they are, you'd be wise to marry the Count. Oh, he's a lovely gentleman. Romeo isn't a patch on him. I really think this second match of yours is far better than your first. In any case, your first is as good as dead. He's no use to you now.

Juliet Do you really mean that?

Nurse Cross my heart!

Juliet Well, that's a great comfort! Go and tell my mother that I have gone to Friar Laurence, to confession, because I have upset my father.

Nurse That's a sensible girl. I'll tell her. [*The **Nurse** goes out*]

Juliet The wicked old woman! The she-devil! I don't know which is worse: encouraging me to break my marriage vows, or running down my husband after praising him so often. I shan't confide in *her* again. I'll go to the Friar for help. If all else fails, I can always kill myself.

ACT FOUR

SCENE 1
Friar Laurence's room

Friar Laurence
Paris
Juliet

[*Friar Laurence* and *Paris* *come in*]

Friar On Thursday, sir? That's very soon.

Paris My father-in-law, Capulet, insists on it, and I'm not exactly anxious to stop him.

Friar You say you don't know what the young lady's feelings are? This is most unusual. I don't like the sound of it.

Paris She has been so upset by Tybalt's death that I have hardly spoken of love. It's not exactly the time for it, is it? Her father thinks it's bad for her to grieve so much, and has wisely brought forward the date of our marriage. He hopes it will stop her brooding. That's the reason for the hurry.

Friar [*To himself*] But I know a reason for delay. How I wish I didn't! [*To Paris*] Look, here she comes.

[*Juliet comes in*]

Paris Well met, my Juliet, my wife.

Juliet That may be, when I *am* your wife.

Paris What may be, must be — on Thursday next.

Juliet And what must be will be.

Friar There's no denying *that*.

Paris Have you come to make confession to Friar Laurence?

Juliet To answer that, I'd have to confess to you.

Paris Don't deny to him that you love me.

Juliet I will confess to *you* that I love *him*. [*To the Friar*] Are you free now, Father? Or shall I come back this evening?

36

Friar I am free now, my poor child. [*To* **Paris**] My lord, I must ask you to leave us.

Paris I wouldn't dream of disturbing your prayers. [*To* **Juliet**] I will wake you early on Thursday, Juliet. Till then, goodbye. [*He kisses her and goes out*]

Juliet Shut the door, Father, and come and weep with me. No-one can help me now.

Friar Oh Juliet, I know all about your troubles, but I can't think how to help you. You are to be married to this Count next Thursday, and nothing will stop it.

Juliet Don't talk about it, Father, unless you can tell me what to do. If you, with all your wisdom, cannot help me, then you must let me use this. [*She takes out a knife*] God joined my heart and Romeo's, you joined our hands. Before I betray this hand and this heart and turn to another, I'll kill myself. So use your experience, wise Father, and tell me what to do. Otherwise this knife will settle the matter.

Friar Wait, daughter. I have an idea. It's a desperate remedy, but no more desperate than your plight. If you have the courage to kill yourself rather than marry the Count, then I think you will dare to do the fearful thing I have in mind.

Juliet Tell me to jump off a tower, or lie among dead men's bones, or get into a newly made grave with a dead body — simply to hear about such things used to make me shudder — and I will do it without fear or question, if it means that I can remain faithful to my sweet love.

Friar Very well, then. Go home, appear cheerful, and agree to marry Paris. Tomorrow is Wednesday. Make sure that you sleep alone tomorrow night. Don't have your nurse with you. [*He goes to a cupboard and gets a bottle*] When you are in bed, drink this. Very soon, you'll feel drowsy and numb. Your heart will seem to stop beating, and the warmth and colour will fade from your face, as if you were dead. You will remain like that for thirty hours, and then you'll wake up, feeling as if you've had a pleasant sleep. So, when Paris comes to wake you on Thursday morning, there you will be, apparently dead. Then, as is the custom of our country, you'll be dressed in your finest clothes and carried, without a coffin, to the tomb of your ancestors. In the meantime, I will write to Romeo and let him know what is happening, and he and I will be there to watch you wake. That very night, Romeo will take you away to Mantua, and you will be free — unless some sudden whim or girlish fear robs you of your courage.

Juliet Give it to me! [*She takes the bottle*] I'm not afraid.

Friar Then go. Be brave! I'll send a Friar to Mantua straight away, with a letter to your husband.

Juliet Love will give me strength! Goodbye, dear Father.

SCENE 2

A room in Capulet's house

[*Capulet*, **Lady Capulet**, *the* **Nurse**, *and three* **Servants** *come in*]

Capulet [*Giving the* **1st Servant** *a list*] Invite these people. [*The* **1st Servant** *goes out.* **Capulet** *speaks to the* **2nd Servant**] Go and hire twenty first-class cooks.

2nd Servant I won't get any bad ones, sir. I'll see if they lick their fingers.

Capulet What? Is that how you judge them?

2nd Servant It's a poor cook that won't taste his own cooking, sir.

Capulet Off you go, then. [*The* **2nd Servant** *goes out*] We'll have a job to be ready. [*To the* **Nurse**] Has my daughter gone to Friar Laurence?

Nurse Yes, she has.

Capulet Well, perhaps he'll be able to make her see some sense, the headstrong little madam.

Nurse Here she comes, back from confession. How cheerful she looks!

[*Juliet comes in*]

Capulet Well, my young Miss! Where have you been gadding?

Juliet I've been to confession, father, and I've learnt how wrong I was to disobey you. The Friar has told me to ask for your forgiveness. [*She kneels down*] I ask your pardon. From now on I will do whatever you say.

Capulet [*To the* **3rd Servant**] Send for Count Paris! Go and tell him! I'll have them married tomorrow morning!

Juliet I met the Count at Friar Laurence's, and behaved towards him as I should.

Capulet I'm glad to hear it. This is much better. Stand up, now. [*Juliet stands up*] This is more like it! Now — Count Paris. Yes, go and fetch him. [*The* **3rd Servant** *goes out*] My goodness! The whole city should be grateful to this Friar!

Juliet Nurse, come to my room with me, to help me sort out what I need for tomorrow.

Lady Capulet No, not tomorrow. Thursday is soon enough.

Capulet Go on, nurse. We'll have the wedding tomorrow. [*Juliet and the* **Nurse** *go out*]

Lady Capulet It's getting late. We'll never be ready.

Capulet I'll see to it. Everything will be all right, I promise you. You go and help Juliet. I shan't go to bed tonight. Let me be the housewife for a change. [*He calls out*] Hello, there! H'm, all the servants are out... Well, I'll walk to the Count's, to warn him about tomorrow. I feel really happy, now that that flighty girl of mine has returned to her senses.

38

SCENE 3
Juliet's bedroom

Juliet
Nurse
Lady Capulet

[*Juliet and the Nurse come in*]

Juliet [*Pointing to a dress*] Yes, that will be best. Dear nurse, please leave me on my own tonight. I must have time to say my prayers — you know how much I need heaven's blessing.

[*Lady Capulet comes in*]

Lady Capulet Are you getting on all right? Do you need any help?

Juliet No thank you, mother. We've sorted out what's needed for tomorrow. So please leave me on my own now. Nurse can be with you. I'm sure you've got your hands full, with this sudden change of plan.

Lady Capulet Good night. Get to bed and rest. You'll need it. [*Lady Capulet and the Nurse go out*]

Juliet Goodbye. God knows when we shall meet again... Oh, I'm so afraid! [*She shivers and puts a shawl round her shoulders*] I'll call them back, to comfort me. Nur — ! [*She stops herself*] How can *she* help? I must do this alone. Now...! [*She picks up the bottle that the Friar gave her*] But what if it doesn't work? Will I be married tomorrow morning? No! [*She puts her knife on the bed*] This will stop it. But what if it is *poison* the Friar has given me, to save himself from blame, because he has already married me to Romeo? I fear it is. But no: he is a holy man. And what if I should wake before Romeo comes? That's a fearful thought. Won't I be stifled by the foul air, and die? Or, if I do survive, won't the deathly darkness and the horror of the ancient tomb, full of the bones of my ancestors, where Tybalt's body lies rotting, where in the night, ghosts... Oh God! Oh God! What if I wake up early, with the horrible smells and the shrieking ghosts, and go mad and start dancing with the skeletons and grab Tybalt from his shroud and dash out my brains? Oh! I think I can see my cousin's ghost, looking for Romeo. Stop, Tybalt! Stop...! [*Pause*] Romeo, Romeo, Romeo, I drink to you. [*She drinks from the bottle, lies down on the bed, and pulls a cover over herself*]

SCENE 4
A room in Capulet's house

Lady Capulet
Nurse
Capulet
2 Servants

[*Lady Capulet comes in, and the Nurse comes hurrying in from the other side*]

Lady Capulet Just a moment, nurse. Take these keys and fetch more spices.

Nurse They're asking for dates and quinces in the kitchen.

[*Capulet comes in*]

Capulet Come along! Come along! It's already three o'clock. [*To the **Nurse***] Go and look after the baking, Angelica. Don't count the cost.

Nurse Get along with you, you house-husband! You'll make yourself ill, staying up all night.

Capulet Rubbish! I've been up all night for less than this before now, and not been ill.

Lady Capulet Yes, you've been a night-bird in your time, but I keep an eye on you nowadays. [***Lady Capulet** and the **Nurse** go out*]

Capulet [*Calling after **Lady Capulet***] Jealous! Jealous! [*Two **Servants** come in, with logs and kitchen equipment*] What have you got there, fellows?

1st Servant Things for the cook, sir. I don't know what they are.

Capulet Hurry up, then, hurry up. [*The **1st Servant** goes out. **Capulet** speaks to the **2nd Servant***] These logs are wet. Fetch some drier ones. Peter will show you where they are.

2nd Servant I don't need Peter, sir. I can find the logs myself: I've got a head.

Capulet So you're a blockhead! Ha! Ha! [*The **2nd Servant** goes out*] Good Lord, it's morning. The Count will be here with the musicians any minute now. [*Music is heard*] There he is. Nurse! Wife! Where are you? Nurse! [*The **Nurse** comes in again*] Go and wake Juliet, and get her ready. I'll go and talk to Paris. Hurry up! The bridegroom's here already.

(Juliet)
Nurse
Lady Capulet
Capulet
Friar Laurence
Paris
—
3 Musicians
Peter

SCENE 5
Juliet's bedroom, then the hall in Capulet's house

[***Juliet** is on the bed. The **Nurse** comes in*]

Nurse Miss! Miss Juliet! Come on, my lady. Why, you *are* a sleepyhead. Sweetheart! Bride! Well, sleep while you can. The Count will make sure you don't get much rest tonight... How soundly she sleeps. But I've got to wake her. Madam! Madam! Well then, let the Count catch you in bed! He'll wake you up! [*She pulls off the cover*] What? Dressed already? I *must* wake you. [*She shakes her*] Lady! Lady! La — Oh, help! My lady's dead. Oh, curse the day that I was born. Some brandy, quick! My lord! My lady!

[***Lady Capulet** comes in*]

Lady Capulet What's all the noise? What's the matter?

Nurse Look! Look!

Lady Capulet Oh, my child, my life! Wake up, or I'll die too!

[*Capulet comes in*]

Capulet Where *is* Juliet? The Count is here.

Nurse She's dead! She's dead!

Lady Capulet Oh God, she's dead.

Capulet What? Let me see. [*He goes to Juliet*] Alas, she is! Death lies on her like an early frost on the sweetest flower in the field. I can say no more.

[*Friar Laurence and Paris come in*]

Friar Is the bride ready to go to church?

Capulet Yes, but never to return. [*To Paris*] My son, death has taken your wife, the night before your wedding day. Death is my son-in-law and my heir. All I have belongs to him.

Paris How I have waited for this morning, and now — this!

Lady Capulet Oh, unhappy day! All I had was just one poor and loving child to find joy and comfort in, and death has snatched her away.

Nurse Oh, day of tears and lamentation.

Paris Death has tricked me, trampled on me. Oh love...! Oh life...!

Capulet Dead! Why *now*, just as we were about to celebrate her marriage? My child is dead, and with her all my joy is buried.

Friar Be quiet! This is no help at all. This girl was yours, but she also belonged to heaven. Now heaven has taken her, and she is all the better for it. You could not save her from death, but heaven has given her eternal life. You wanted happiness for her here on earth. Why are you weeping, now that she has gained the highest joy in heaven? Have you so little love for her? It is not always the longest marriages that are the best. Dry your tears, lay your flowers on her, and carry her to church in her finest clothes, according to our custom. It is natural that we should weep, but reason laughs at our tears.

Capulet Our joy has turned to sorrow, our wedding celebration to a burial feast, and our hymns to mournful music. And our bridal flowers will deck Juliet's grave.

Friar [*To them all*] Prepare to follow Juliet to the tomb. The heavens are angry with you. Don't offend them further.

[*They place flowers on Juliet's body as they go out*]

[*The scene now changes to the hall in Capulet's house. Three Musicians come in*]

1st Musician We might as well pack up our instruments and go.

[*Peter comes in*]

Peter Play us a tune, lads! I feel sad, and a cheerful wail will comfort me.

1st Musician "Wail", indeed! This is no time for playing.

Peter If you won't play, then this is how I'll pay you. [*He makes a rude gesture*] You fiddler!

1st Musician "Fiddler", indeed. You third-rate servant!

Peter Then I'll try out my carving knife on your head. [*He pulls out a dagger*] I won't put up with your screeching. I'll "do, re, me" you. Make a note of that!

2nd Musician Why don't you put your knife away, and show us your wit instead?

Peter [*He puts the dagger away*] Right! See how this strikes you. [*He sings*]
When sadness grips the aching heart,
And you are in a doleful dump,
Then music's silver sound —
Why "silver sound"? What do *you* think, Simon Catgut?

1st Musician I suppose, because silver has a sweet sound, sir.

Peter Mmm. And what do you say, Hugh Fiddler?

2nd Musician Because musicians play for money, sir.

Peter And what do you say, James Soundpost?

3rd Musician I don't know what to say, sir.

Peter Oh, I forgot. You are only a singer. I'll have to speak for you. It's silver because musicians never get gold for their noises. [*He sings as he goes out*]
Then music's silver sound will soothe
The sadness of a broken heart.

1st Musician What a pest that fellow is!

2nd Musician Forget him! We'll go in and wait for the mourners, and stay for dinner.

42

ACT FIVE

SCENE 1

A street in Mantua, near where Romeo is staying

Romeo
Balthasar
Apothecary

[*Romeo comes in*]

Romeo If my dreams are to be trusted, something good will happen today. I dreamt that my love came and found me dead, and brought me to life with her kisses, and I was an emperor. What a strange dream, that lets a dead man think! Oh, how sweet love is, when even dreams of love are so full of joy. [*Balthasar, Romeo's servant, comes in*] Ah! News from Verona! Well, Balthasar, have you got a letter for me from the Friar? How is my lady? Is my father well? How *is* my Juliet? Nothing can be wrong, if she is well.

Balthasar Then she is well. Her body lies in the Capulets' tomb, and her soul is with the angels. I saw her laid there, and came to tell you straight away. Please forgive me for bringing such sad news.

Romeo Is that so? Then I defy you, stars! [*Pause*] You know where I'm staying. Get me a pen and some paper, and hire some horses. I'll leave Mantua tonight.

Balthasar Please calm yourself, sir. Don't do anything rash.

Romeo Nonsense, man! Go and do what I told you to. Are there *really* no letters from the Friar?

Balthasar No, sir.

Romeo Never mind. Go and hire the horses. I'll join you soon. [*Balthasar goes out*] Well, Juliet, I shall lie with you tonight. Let me see: what do I need...? Desperate thoughts come easily to desperate men. I remember seeing a poor apothecary who lives near here, collecting herbs for his medicines. He was dressed in rags, thin, and worn down by his poverty. He had a few odds and ends in his shop: skins of animals, empty boxes, pots, a few seeds, all spread out to make some sort of show. I remember thinking that if a man wanted some poison, this poor creature would sell it to him, even though the penalty is death. So, the thought came before the need! [*He walks a little way along the street*] Ah! This must be his shop. [*He bangs on a door*] Hello there!

Apothecary [*From inside his house*] Who's that?

Romeo Come here, man. [*The Apothecary comes out*] I can see you are poor. Look, here's forty pounds. [*Romeo shows him the money*] Let me have some poison, something that will act quickly, and snuff out a poor man's life.

43

Apothecary I have such poisons, but it's illegal to sell them.

Romeo What? Are you afraid to die, and you so poor and your life so wretched? The world is no friend to you. Its laws won't make you rich, so break the law and take this. [*He shows him the money again*]

Apothecary It's only my poverty that makes me do it. [*He goes into his house*]

Romeo Then I'll pay your poverty.

Apothecary [*He comes out again and gives **Romeo** a bottle*] Drink this, and if you had the strength of twenty men, it would kill you.

Romeo There you are. [*He gives him the money*] That stuff is far worse poison to men's souls than the poor concoctions that you're not allowed to sell. Go and buy some food, and fatten yourself up. [*The **Apothecary** goes into his house. **Romeo** holds up the poison*] Come, sweet drink! Come with me to Juliet's grave. That's where I must use you.

SCENE 2

Friar Laurence's room

| Friar John |
| Friar Laurence |

[***Friar John** comes running in*]

Friar John [*Calling out*] Brother Laurence!

[***Friar Laurence** comes in*]

Friar Laurence Friar John! Welcome back from Mantua! What does Romeo say? Or has he written?

Friar John [*Hurriedly*] I went to find another Friar to go with me to Mantua, but he was visiting some people who were ill, and the disease turned out to be infectious, so they wouldn't let us out of the house. I never got to Mantua!

Friar Laurence Then who took my letter to Romeo?

Friar John I couldn't send it — here it is. I couldn't even get a messenger to bring it to you, they were so worried about the infection.

Friar Laurence Oh, dear God! That letter was important. We may be in grave danger now... Friar John, go and find a crowbar, and bring it to my room.

Friar John I'll bring it straight away, Brother. [*He goes out*]

Friar Laurence I shall have to go to the tomb on my own. Juliet will wake up within the next three hours, and she'll be angry with me for not letting Romeo know what's been happening. But I'll write to him again, and keep Juliet with me until he comes. Poor girl, shut up in a dead man's tomb!

Paris	Prince Escalus
His servant	(Attendants)
Romeo	Citizens
Balthasar	Capulet
Juliet	Lady Capulet
(Tybalt dead)	(Their friends)
Friar Laurence	Montague
3 Officers	(His friends)
(Other Officers)	

SCENE 3

A churchyard. In front of the tomb of the Capulets*

[*Paris* comes in with his **Servant**, who is carrying a lantern and some flowers]

Paris Give me the lantern, boy, and go and wait over there. [*He points*] No — blow it out, I don't want to be seen. Go and lie under those yew trees over there, and put your ear to the ground. If anyone comes, you'll hear their footsteps. Whistle if you hear anything. Give me the flowers. Now go.

Servant [*He blows out the lantern, and speaks to himself as he goes to the side of the stage and lies down*] I'm scared, but I'll do it.

Paris Sweet flower, I lay my flowers upon
    Your wedding bed of earth and stone
    Each night I'll weep upon your tomb,
    And pray for you, now you are gone.
[*The* **Servant** *whistles*] Someone's coming! Who the devil can it be, disturbing my prayers? And carrying a light! I must hide. [*He hides*]

[*Romeo* comes in with **Balthasar**, who is carrying a crowbar and a lantern]

Romeo Give me that crowbar. [*He takes it*] Take this letter, and deliver it to my father first thing in the morning. Give me the lantern. Now, keep out of the way, and don't interfere, whatever you see or hear. I'm going into the tomb to look at my lady, and take a precious ring from her finger. Now go! If you come back and spy on me, I swear I'll tear you limb from limb.

Balthasar I'll go, sir. I won't trouble you.

Romeo That's a good fellow. Take this [*he gives him money*] and use it well. Goodbye, my friend.

Balthasar [*To himself*] I don't like the look of this. I'll go and hide. [*He hides*]

Romeo [*He speaks as he breaks the tomb open*] You cradle of death! You horrible glutton, fed with the sweetest creature that ever lived! I'll force your rotten jaws open, and cram you with more food!

*See note on Page 52.

Paris [*To himself*] This must be the Montague who was banished, the one who murdered my Juliet's cousin, Tybalt. I'm sure he's up to no good. I'll arrest him. [*He comes out and speaks to **Romeo***] Stop, you villain! Can revenge be taken beyond the grave? Come with me, for you must die.

Romeo Die? That's what I came here for, my friend! Go! Let the dead frighten you away. Don't tempt me to commit another sin. Go away, save yourself. You can say a madman told you to run away.

Paris I will not! I arrest you as a criminal. [*He draws his sword*]

Romeo Well, you've only yourself to blame. [*He draws his sword and they fight*]

Paris's Servant Oh Lord! I'll go and call the officers.

Paris [***Romeo** wounds him, and he speaks as he dies*] You've killed me! If you have any mercy, open the tomb, and lay me beside Juliet.

Romeo Indeed I will. Let me look at you. Why, it's Mercutio's cousin, Count Paris! What was it my servant said as we were riding here? Didn't he tell me Paris was going to marry Juliet? Or have I gone crazy and imagined it? [*To **Paris***] Fortune has made fools of us both. I'll bury you in a glorious grave. [*He opens the tomb*] This is no grave, it is bright with Juliet's beauty. [*He puts **Paris**'s body in the tomb*] Buried by a dead man! Hm! What a time to make a joke. Like a flash of lightning before the dark... [*He looks at **Juliet***] O, my love, my wife. Death has had no power over your beauty. [*He sees **Tybalt**'s body*] Ah, Tybalt! What more can I do for you than kill myself, with the same hand that robbed you of your youth? Forgive me, cousin. Ah, dear Juliet, why are you still so lovely? Is that monster death in love with you, and keeping you here in the dark for himself? Then I'll stay with you for ever, and shake off this ill-fated life of mine. A last look, a last kiss... [*He embraces and kisses her, and then holds up the bottle of poison*] Guide this weary and life-sick body of mine to destruction. Here's to my love! [*He drinks and shudders*] How quickly the poison works...! So, with a kiss, I die. [*He falls dead beside **Juliet***]

[***Friar Laurence** comes in with a lantern and a crowbar. He stumbles at the side of the stage, near where **Balthasar** is hiding*]

Friar Oh, the number of times I've tripped over these graves! [*He sees **Balthasar***] Who's there?

Balthasar It's me — a friend.

Friar God bless you! Tell me, my friend, what is that lantern over there, wasting its light on worms and empty skulls? It seems to be in the Capulets' tomb.

Balthasar That's right, sir. My master, Romeo, is in there.

Friar How long has he been there?

Balthasar A good half hour.

Friar Come with me. [*He starts going towards the tomb*]

Balthasar I daren't, sir. My master thinks I've gone away. He threatened to kill me if I stayed and watched him.

Friar Stay here, then. Oh God! I wonder if —

Balthasar While I was lying here, I dreamt that my master fought and killed someone.

Friar What? Romeo? [*He goes forward and sees blood and swords on the ground*] Dear God! What's all this blood? And these swords, in a holy place like this! [*He goes into the tomb*] Romeo! So pale... And who's this? Paris! Covered in blood! What cruel fate is responsible for this? [*Juliet stirs*] She's moving...

Juliet Oh, kind Father! Where is my husband? I remember now where I was meant to be, and here I am. Where is my Romeo?

[*The **Officers** are heard approaching*]

Friar I can hear someone coming. Lady, come out of this gruesome place. Some greater power has upset our plans. Come, your husband is dead — there he is, beside you — and Paris too. Come, I'll take you to a convent. There's no time for questions, the Officers are coming. Come, Juliet. I daren't stay any longer.

Juliet I shan't leave. You can go. [*The **Friar** runs out with his crowbar*] What's this? [*She takes the bottle from **Romeo**'s hand*] Poison? Oh, my cruel love, have you drunk it all, and left no friendly drop for me? Perhaps I'll find some on your lips. [*She kisses him*] Your lips are warm!

Officers [*Off stage*] Go on, boy! Which way?

Juliet They're coming. I'll be quick. [*She takes **Romeo**'s dagger*] Oh lucky dagger, I'll be your sheath. [*She stabs herself and dies*]

[***Paris's Servant** comes in with some **Officers***]

Servant That's the place, where the light is.

1st Officer There's blood on the ground. Search the churchyard. Arrest anyone you find. [*Some **Officers** go out*] Oh, my God, here's Count Paris, murdered... And Juliet, who was laid here yesterday, bleeding and still warm. Go and tell the Prince! Run to the Capulets! Call the Montagues!

[*Some **Officers** come in with **Balthasar***]

2nd Officer Here's Romeo's servant. We found him in the churchyard.

1st Officer Hold him there until the Prince comes. [***Balthasar** is taken to one side*]

[***Friar Laurence** is brought in by two **Officers**. One of them is carrying a crowbar*]

3rd Officer We found this Friar going out of the churchyard, carrying this crowbar. He was trembling and weeping.

1st Officer Very suspicious. Keep him there too. [*The **Friar** is taken to where **Balthasar** is being held*]

[**Prince Escalus** *comes in with his* **Attendants** *and some* **Citizens**]

Prince What's been happening, so early in the morning?

[**Capulet** *comes in with* **Lady Capulet** *and some* **Friends**]

Capulet What are they all shouting about?

Lady Capulet I've heard people shouting "Romeo", "Juliet", "Paris", and running towards our tomb.

Prince What's all this noise and panic?

1st Officer [*To the* **Prince**] My lord, here is Paris, murdered; Romeo, dead; and Juliet, who was buried yesterday, warm and only just killed. And we found this Friar, and Romeo's servant, carrying tools.

Capulet [*He sees* **Juliet**'s *body*] O heavens! Wife, look how our daughter lies bleeding, with Romeo's dagger in her breast.

Lady Capulet Ah me — this reminds me of my own mortality.

[**Montague** *comes in with some* **Friends**]

Prince Montague, your son has been brought down.

Montague My lord, my wife is dead, grieving for her exiled son. What more sorrows do I have to face in my old age?

Prince [*He points at* **Romeo**'s *body*] Look there, and you'll see.

Montague [*He goes into the tomb*] Bad mannered boy, pushing ahead of your father to the grave!

Prince Contain your grief and anger, until we have found out exactly what has happened. Then I will join with you in mourning... Who are the suspects?

Friar I seem to be the most likely suspect, though I have done the least. I plead both guilty and innocent.

Prince Then tell us what you know.

Friar I'll be brief. Romeo, lying there dead, was Juliet's husband, and she was Romeo's faithful wife. I married them secretly, and on that very day Tybalt was killed and Romeo banished. It was for Romeo, not for Tybalt, that Juliet pined. To stop her grief, Capulet would have married her to Paris. It was then she came to me, desperate, ready to kill herself. I gave her a drug to make her sleep. She took it and appeared to be dead. In the meantime I wrote to Romeo, asking him to come here tonight, but my letter did not reach him. At the time when Juliet was due to wake up, I came here to take her away — I meant to keep her safe, until I could send for Romeo. But when I got here, I found noble Paris, and faithful Romeo, both dead. Juliet woke up, and I begged her to accept her fate and come with me. She refused, a noise frightened me, and I ran off. It seems the poor desperate girl then killed herself. Her nurse knew about the marriage, and if any of this was my fault, then let me die.

Prince I have always known you to be a good man. [*To the **Officers***] Where is Romeo's servant? What has he to say?

Balthasar I took my master news of Juliet's death, and he came here from Mantua as quickly as he could. [*He takes a letter out of his pocket*] He told me to give this letter to his father, and threatened to kill me unless I went away and left him.

Prince Give me the letter. I will look at it. Where is the Count's servant, the one who raised the alarm? [***Paris's Servant** comes forward*] Fellow, what was your master doing here?

Paris's Servant He came here to put flowers on his lady's grave, and told me to keep watch. Then someone came with a lantern to open the tomb, and my master attacked him and I ran away to call the Officers.

Prince [*He looks at the letter*] This letter confirms the Friar's story. Romeo says he bought poison and came here to die, to be with Juliet... Come here, Capulet. And you, Montague. [*They step forward*] See what your hate has led to! Their love has killed your joy. And I have lost two of my own family, because I turned a blind eye on your quarrel. We have all been punished.

Capulet Brother Montague, give me your hand. [*They shake hands*] Your friendship is all I ask for.

Montague But I can give you more. I will make a statue of Juliet in pure gold, and as long as Verona is Verona, no-one will be better remembered than faithful Juliet.

Capulet And I will make as rich a statue of Romeo to lie beside her — poor victims of our hate.

Prince This morning brings with it a sad and gloomy peace. Even the sun refuses to show his face for sorrow. Go now, and talk of these sad events. Some of you shall be pardoned, others punished. For never has there been a sadder story than this of Romeo and his Juliet.

THE END

A NOTE ON THE TIME SCHEME IN "ROMEO AND JULIET"

Shakespeare's play begins on a Sunday morning at about nine o'clock, and ends very early the following Thursday morning. A large number of events are packed into these few days, and most of them are at specific times. On the first day, the street fighting takes place soon after nine, the party at the Capulets' is that evening, the balcony scene is that night. Early on Monday, Romeo meets Friar Laurence. At noon he sees the Nurse, and by early afternoon he and Juliet are married. That same afternoon, Mercutio and Tybalt are killed, Romeo is banished, and the lovers are in despair. But the Friar and the Nurse arrange for Romeo to come to Juliet that night. In the evening, Capulet decides that Juliet and Paris will be married on Thursday, and he tells his wife to inform Juliet of his decision. She does not do so, however. She waits until the following morning.

On Tuesday morning, at dawn, Romeo leaves Juliet. Juliet's mother then comes in and tells Juliet that she is to marry Paris. Juliet goes to Friar Laurence for help, and is given the potion and told to make her peace with her father. (Shakespeare makes the Friar say that Juliet will wake after forty-two hours, a time that does not seem to be at all relevant. In this version, we have the Friar saying "thirty hours".) When Juliet goes to her father it is already evening, although it seems as if she has come straight from the Friar. So the events of this day do not follow a logical pattern. Capulet brings the wedding forward to the following day, Wednesday, and Juliet drinks the potion while the household prepares for the celebration.

Wednesday is crowded with events. Early in the morning, Juliet is found, apparently dead. She is placed in the tomb, presumably in the morning, since Romeo's servant Balthasar has to have time to ride to Mantua and tell Romeo what has happened. Romeo than rides with him back to Verona, and arrives at the tomb late at night. The Friar arrives a little later, since Juliet is due to wake in the early hours of the morning (i.e. after thirty hours). The events at the tomb end with the Prince's arrival, by which time dawn is breaking on Thursday.

In Shakespeare's text, the Watch (Officers) say that Juliet has been in the tomb for two days. This has been altered to "since yesterday", to fit in with the logical time scheme. This is not, of course, to say that Shakespeare's words here and elsewhere are not dramatically effective.

A NOTE ON THE CAPULETS' TOMB

The tomb in the last scene of "Romeo and Juliet" can be a problem for both readers and producers of the play. The tomb is clearly a large stone structure with room for the remains of generations of Capulets, with an entrance that allows people to walk in and out quite easily. The entrance must be securely closed, but able to be opened with a crowbar. When it is open, enough of the inside must be disclosed for the audience to see Juliet's body and, a little later, the bodies of Paris and Romeo. So the entrance could consist of two locked wooden doors, and Romeo could break the lock with his crowbar and open them. This presents obvious difficulties for stage production, since an elaborate set would be required.

The other difficulties arise from Shakespeare's text, parts of which are inconsistent with the description of the tomb just given. For example, both the Friar and Romeo equip themselves with spades (or mattocks) as well as crowbars. Why is this? Also, Paris strews flowers (and sprinkles water) on Juliet's "grave". This hardly fits with the picture one has in one's mind of Juliet being in a "vault" (a word used in the text). The word "buried" also presents a problem, suggesting as it does a body in the earth. Such difficulties are, of course, easily overcome by the imagination of a reader. It is the producer of the play on the stage who has to work out a solution that is both acceptable to an audience and a fair representation of the play as written.

In this version of the play, we have, rightly or wrongly, tried to use words which minimise the inconsistencies.